# Recreation Programming
# and Activities
# For Older Adults

By

Jerold E. Elliott, Re. D.

and

Judith A. Sorg-Elliott, M. S.

Art Director:  Sandra Sikorski
Cover Design:  Pam Heidtmann
Production:  Bonnie Godbey
Printing and Binding:  BookCrafters, Chelsea, MI

Library of Congress Catalogue Card Number  91-66104
ISBN 0-910251-46-0

# Recreation Programming and Activities For Older Adults

This book is dedicated to the participants of the over one hundred fifty
"Judy and Jerry show" workshops.
Thank you for your encouragement and support.


Judy and Jerry Elliott

# About the Authors

*Jerold E. Elliott* recently retired from the Pennsylvania State University as an associate professor in the Department of Leisure Studies. He continues to use his more than thirty years of experience in the recreation field through his recreation consulting service for a variety of groups and agencies.

*Judith A. Sorg-Elliott* is an assistant professor in the Department of Recreation at Lock Haven University of Pennsylvania. Recreation programming, therapeutic recreation and marketing are her major teaching responsibilities. Her experience as a therapeutic recreation professional included directing the program at a 600-bed county nursing home.

Jerry and Judy Elliott have been designing recreation programs for the elderly for more than twelve years. They combined their knowledge and expertise to provide the recreation professional with high quality, practical information through Penn State's Continuing Education Program. They have conducted more than 150 workshops on recreation for the elderly with the following titles:

> Recreation Programming for Older Adults,
> Activities That Promote Exercise,
> Recreation for Higher Level Older Adults,
> Dance and Dramatics for Older Adults,
> Horticulture Activities in Therapeutic Recreation,
> Public Relations and More: A Program for Health-Care Providers and
> > Human Service Personnel,
> Another Look at Crafts, and
> Evaluating Therapeutic Recreation Programs for the Older Adult.

Their six-hour workshops received the approval of the Pennsylvania and Ohio State Boards of Examinations of Nursing Home Administrators. Participants from Pennsylvania, Ohio, Delaware and New Jersey with backgrounds in Therapeutic Recreation, Activities, Occupation and Physical Therapy, as well as nursing and administration have attended their workshops.

The authors have presented programs for the Pennsylvania Area Agency on Aging, Pennsylvania Therapeutic Recreation Society, Pennsylvania Recreation and Parks Society, Pennsylvania Association for Health, Physical Education, Recreation and Dance, and the mid-Atlantic Region of the National Association for Interpretation.

The material compiled for these many programs provides the basis for this publication.

# TABLE OF CONTENTS

# INTRODUCTION

This book has been written to help the recreation professional design quality recreation programs for nursing home clients. It covers program design, activity scheduling, documentation, and recreation program review.

Anyone providing recreation for older adults may find this material helpful, although the publication was designed primarily for usage in nursing homes servicing intermediate and skilled care clients.

Quality program design is covered in the early chapters while the later chapters describe workable activities to implement the program. Some of the activities are old favorites that have been around for years, but are included because many of these "old friends" are new to some leaders.

Many new activities as well as modifications of old favorites are included. Although all of these activities have been utilized with nursing home clients, additional modifications may be desirable to benefit a particular group or setting.

It is hoped that the ideas presented in this book will assist in the development of an innovative and challenging recreation program.

> The authors and publisher caution the professional to be sensitive to the abilities and limitations of the participants. The nature of some activities may not be appropriate for your clients. Professional judgment on your part is required.

Jerold E. Elliott, Re. D
Associate Professor (Retired)
Department of Leisure Studies
Pennsylvania State University
University Park, PA

Judith Sorg-Elliott, M. S.
Assistant Professor
Department of Recreation
Lock Haven University
Lock Haven, PA

# ACHIEVING A BALANCED PROGRAM

# ACHIEVING A BALANCED PROGRAM

The contemporary nursing home is a full-care facility. As such it must not only care for the residents' physical needs but also for their intellectual and social needs. The stereotype of people sitting around in wheelchairs and rockers staring off into space is no longer justified or acceptable. A quality program includes personal comfort, suitable physical activity, adequate mental stimulation and an opportunity for social interaction for each client.

## The Team Approach

Quality care is dependent upon a team approach to planning and the provision of services. Only with input from all of the disciplines can a plan of care be devised for the "whole" person. Recreation activities based on the clients' needs and interests are a vital link in the chain of quality care. As a part of the team of care givers, Therapeutic Recreation focuses on the strengths of the client to lessen the frustrations of growing older.

## The Program Continuum

Some nursing home recreation programs provide only diversional activities which are scheduled to fill time in the clients' day. At the other end of the spectrum of recreation are programs which are totally treatment oriented. All of the clients are seen on a one-to-one basis as prescribed by a physician in order to treat a weakness. If recreation programming is visualized on a continuum, with diversional activities at one end and the treatment approach at the other, a balanced program would fall somewhere in the middle. Programs would be scheduled to assist each individual client reach his/her fullest potential, with activities that would provide opportunities for socialization and mental stimulation as well as enjoyment. There would also be experiences designed for the individual client based upon his or her needs and interests as opposed to those of the staff. All recreation programming would involve a bit of fun as well as treatment, thereby being therapeutic in nature.

Whether the program is called "Activities," "Recreation," or "Therapeutic Recreation," it can provide a client with a sense of accomplishment or achievement that is often missing as one grows older.

## Client-Oriented Recreation

To be therapeutic, a recreation program must have balance as well as being client-oriented. Providing clients with the opportunity to function to the best of their present abilities is the concept behind the client-oriented recreation program. This includes the lowest level client who does not respond to his or her own name as well as the client who needs a minimal amount of care.

The following Client-Oriented Therapeutic Recreation Program Model [Figure 1] is based on the work of Farrell and Lundegren (1991) and will be utilized throughout this book.

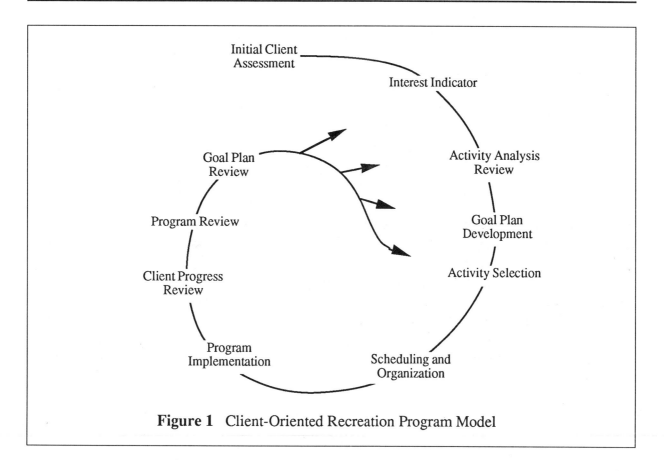

**Figure 1**   Client-Oriented Recreation Program Model

## Program Model Overview

Every program must begin with the client's needs and interests.  Assessing each client's functional level within the physical, cognitive and social/affective areas is the first step.  A review of both the client's strengths and weaknesses must be completed.

The clients' interests are just as important as their functional level and must be considered before any programming is planned.  Prior to the development of a goal or treatment plan, the appropriate types of activities must be selected to meet the needs and interests of the client. Unfortunately in some nursing home recreation programs, these steps are not employed.  The clients attend programs which have been in place for years with little or no regard being given to the individual client's needs or interests, or for the inherent values of the activity.  Only after careful review of the benefits within each recreation activity, should the decision be made as to which activities would best suit the clients' interests and needs.

The next steps of scheduling, organization and implementation each affect the client's progress. An enthusiastic motivated staff of professionals and volunteers is a necessity for a balanced program.

Every step of the process, from assessing client's needs through activity selection and program implementation must be evaluated.  Without evaluation it is impossible to determine program effectiveness.

## Quality Assurance And Recreation

The process known as Quality Assurance has been developed to assist in monitoring of care within the nursing home setting. Quality Assurance is a series of standards which are used to evaluate all aspects of nursing home care. Although Quality Assurance was developed for the entire nursing home, the standards for recreation provide a starting place for monitoring the recreation program. Like all standards, those under Quality Assurance are minimal rather than optimal requirements. The recreation department should reach beyond the suggested Quality Assurance standards.

Each of the following chapters addresses various aspects of the Client-Oriented Program Model in more detail. Chapter 2 explores client assessment techniques. It has suggestions for assessing both needs and interests, as well as sample forms which make the information readily available to the recreation professional.

Chapter 2 also provides the procedure for analyzing the inherent value of activities . This analysis will assist in selecting appropriate activities to meet the clients' needs and interests. This analysis will aid the recreation staff member in the quest to utilize professional terminology at team planning sessions.

Succeeding chapters describe goal planning, organization and scheduling, and of course, evaluation techniques.

## Summary

There is a growing need to provide quality programming based upon individualized client needs. This task becomes more formidable every day as the client's entry functioning level declines. Faced with this dilemma, nursing home staff need to remember the overall goal of helping each client to live to his/her fullest potential regardless of functioning level. In other words, *to be alive as long as they live* is the goal for all clients. The need is there for challenging, innovative, quality care which preserves the individuality and dignity of the client. Therapeutic Recreation has an important contribution to make to this total team effort. Innovative programming by a dedicated recreation staff which involves all residents on regular basis is one key to meeting this important goal.

# Resources

### The Older Adult

Feil, N. (1982). *Validation: The Feil Method*. Cleveland, OH: Edward Feil Productions.

Fish, H. V. (1971). *Activities Program for Senior Citizens*. West Nyack, NY: Parker Publishing Company:

Merrill, T. (1967). *Activities for the Aged and Infirm*. Springfield, IL: Charles C. Thomas Publishers.

National Recreation and Parks Association. (1983). *Aging and Leisure*. Alexandria, VA.

Teaff, J. D. (1985). *Leisure Services with the Elderly*. Times Mirror/Mosby College Publishing: St. Louis, MO,

U.S. Department of Health, Education and Welfare. *Activity Coordinator's Guide*. Washington, DC.

### Therapeutic Recreation

Peterson, C. A. and Gunn, S. L., (1984). *Therapeutic Recreation Program Design*: *Principles and Procedures*. (2nd ed.) Englewood Cliffs, NJ: Prentice-Hall Inc.

O'Morrow, G. (1980). *Therapeutic Recreation: A Helping Profession*. Reston, VA: Reston Publishing.

Peterson, C. A. (1978). *Characteristics of Special Populations*. Washington, DC: Hawkins and Associates Inc.

### Recreation Programming

Edginton, C. R. Compton, H., and Hanson, C. (1980). *Recreation and Leisure Programming: A Guide for the Professional*. Philadelphia, PA: Saunders College Publishing.

Edginton, C. R. and Griffith, C. A. (1983). *The Recreation and Leisure Service Delivery System*. Philadelphia, PA: Saunders College Publishing.

Farrell, P. and Lundegren, H. (1991). *The Process of Recreation Programming*. (3rd ed.) State College, PA: Venture Publishing, Inc.

Graham, P. J. and Klar, L. R. (1979). *Planning and Delivering Leisure Services*. Dubuque, IA: William C. Brown Company Publishers.

## NOTES

# CLIENT ASSESSMENT AND ACTIVITY SELECTION

Initial Assessment

Staff Observation Scale

Assessment Tool Administration

Interest Indicators

Interest Survey Format

Activity Analysis

Program Analysis

Summary

Resources

# CLIENT ASSESSMENT AND ACTIVITY SELECTION

Whenever a client enters a facility there is usually a flurry of paper work being completed. In the first few days the clients are often visited and questioned by representatives from all of the disciplines.

## Initial Assessment

Many of the professionals in the field of therapeutic recreation prefer to give clients a week to adjust to their surroundings before beginning client assessments. Others prefer to complete assessments within twenty four hours of admission. Either procedure is acceptable, however, it should be noted that client assessment is usually the first step in getting to know the client. If that step is postponed for too long the process is more difficult for everyone and the therapeutic recreation professionals miss an opportunity to assist the client during the adjustment period. Too often recreation professionals look at assessments as additional paper work, instead of recognizing the reality that the assessment should be the key to assisting clients to function at their maximum level.

There are many types of client assessment tools on the market and many facilities have developed their own. Because there is growing concern for a minimal set of assessment standards, the MDS (Minimum Data Set) has been developed. It is a requirement for all nursing facilities that participate in Medicare and Medicaid programs. Remember, the MDS is a minimal set of standards and needs to be supplemented with additional information relating to recreation. It is important the type of assessment used is easy to administer and utilized for planning purposes. In addition, OBRA regulations need to be addressed for all assessments. A sixteen page assessment form for each client may be extremely thorough, but on a day to day basis it is not feasible because of its length. The staff complete such an assessment, then file it away without referring to it again. A one to two page assessment tool is best when compiling goal plans or progress notes.

Often a Social Service or Admissions employee has compiled data on the client prior to admission. Recreation personnel should refer to these notes and any nursing materials before compiling another profile. It seems most appropriate to utilize a team approach when compiling client assessments.

Whatever form the assessment takes, it should be kept as positive as possible. For example, instead of "client can not walk" use "client ambulates via wheelchair." This positive approach acts as a reminder to always think of the clients' strengths.

The assessment tool should assist with goal development and not hinder it, therefore the assessment should be easy to administer and read. Check lists, scales, and one word fill-in forms are much easier to use than those which require extensive writing by the recreation professional. The assessment tool should include some of the clients' background as well as present functioning level. Assessments are required to include a leisure interest section, detailing strengths/ weaknesses and needs. Leisure interest indicators will be discussed on page 11.

## Staff Observation Scale

The following Staff Observation Scale (SOS) [Figure 2] was developed as an easy to administer assessment tool which is written in positive language and is quickly completed. It can be utilized upon admission, with a follow-up on the same form in a few weeks or months. Different colors of pen would help to separate the two assessments. The degree of change and the direction of that change is easily determined.

## Assessment Tool Administration

When administering an assessment tool, approach the client as if this were a visit as opposed to an interview. Memorize the type of information needed so the session can be conducted without having to refer to the actual instrument. The experience should be pleasant for the client; any notes should be written after leaving the clients' room. It is impossible to remember everything in one session so visit several times before finishing the assessment. Although it would be possible to take the form into the client's room in order to complete it in one session, this does nothing to aid the clients' adjustment. Conducting the session as a conversation versus an interview helps build a trusting relationship. By taking the time to do the assessment over several visits, the client begins to know the recreation professional and a rapport is established. The recreation professional, in turn, has a more complete profile of the client which makes it easier to develop appropriate goal statements.

## Interest Indicators

Often the only information available about client upon admission is the initial report which was compiled by a social worker or admissions counselor. These reports usually profile the type of work the client did, as well as past and present leisure interests. This report should be the starting point for determining the leisure interests of the client.

After the recreation professional has met the client and completed the initial assessment, a leisure interest survey may be in order. A leisure interest survey will assist the therapeutic recreation personnel in planning activities for that specific client.

Remembering that some people derived great enjoyment from their work, a section should be included in the survey which obtains additional work information. A survey which consists of checklists of activities without any additional information may end up as a wasted piece of paper if the client refuses to participate. The interest survey must give some indication as to whether or not client prefers to engage in activities in his or her room, alone, or with others. Vital information in terms of best time of day, preferred setting as well as other participants will make a difference in activity planning.

In many cases, a familiar activity from the past is no longer feasible in the client's present condition. It then becomes the recreation professional's job to determine what activity is similar enough to be of interest to the client. For example the client who can no longer quilt may be the perfect person to teach another how to quilt. Or, she may be asked to identify different quilt patterns. The person who was fond of bridge may learn how to play an easier card game. A man

## Staff Observation Scale

Client_____ Date_____ Rater _____

Evaluate the client on the following basis: 0 = Never; 2 = Sometimes (20 percent); 4 = Often (40 percent); 6 = Very Often (60 percent); 8 = Usually (80 percent); 10 = Always (100 percent)

**Physical Condition**                                   **Comments:**

| body flexibility | 0 | 1 | 2 | 3 | 4 | 5 | 6 | 7 | 8 | 9 | 10 |
| arms/hands-range of motion | 0 | 1 | 2 | 3 | 4 | 5 | 6 | 7 | 8 | 9 | 10 |
| legs/feet-range of motion | 0 | 1 | 2 | 3 | 4 | 5 | 6 | 7 | 8 | 9 | 10 |
| endurance | 0 | 1 | 2 | 3 | 4 | 5 | 6 | 7 | 8 | 9 | 10 |
| coordination-body parts | 0 | 1 | 2 | 3 | 4 | 5 | 6 | 7 | 8 | 9 | 10 |
| eye/hand coordination | 0 | 1 | 2 | 3 | 4 | 5 | 6 | 7 | 8 | 9 | 10 |
| self locomotion | 0 | 1 | 2 | 3 | 4 | 5 | 6 | 7 | 8 | 9 | 10 |
| sight | 0 | 1 | 2 | 3 | 4 | 5 | 6 | 7 | 8 | 9 | 10 |
| hearing | 0 | 1 | 2 | 3 | 4 | 5 | 6 | 7 | 8 | 9 | 10 |
| _____ | 0 | 1 | 2 | 3 | 4 | 5 | 6 | 7 | 8 | 9 | 10 |
| _____ | 0 | 1 | 2 | 3 | 4 | 5 | 6 | 7 | 8 | 9 | 10 |

**Self Care**

| daily grooming | 0 | 1 | 2 | 3 | 4 | 5 | 6 | 7 | 8 | 9 | 10 |
| toilet use | 0 | 1 | 2 | 3 | 4 | 5 | 6 | 7 | 8 | 9 | 10 |
| bathing | 0 | 1 | 2 | 3 | 4 | 5 | 6 | 7 | 8 | 9 | 10 |
| eating | 0 | 1 | 2 | 3 | 4 | 5 | 6 | 7 | 8 | 9 | 10 |
| _____ | 0 | 1 | 2 | 3 | 4 | 5 | 6 | 7 | 8 | 9 | 10 |
| _____ | 0 | 1 | 2 | 3 | 4 | 5 | 6 | 7 | 8 | 9 | 10 |

**Cognitive Aspects**

| concentration | 0 | 1 | 2 | 3 | 4 | 5 | 6 | 7 | 8 | 9 | 10 |
| awareness | 0 | 1 | 2 | 3 | 4 | 5 | 6 | 7 | 8 | 9 | 10 |
| verbalization | 0 | 1 | 2 | 3 | 4 | 5 | 6 | 7 | 8 | 9 | 10 |
| short term memory | 0 | 1 | 2 | 3 | 4 | 5 | 6 | 7 | 8 | 9 | 10 |
| long term memory | 0 | 1 | 2 | 3 | 4 | 5 | 6 | 7 | 8 | 9 | 10 |
| smell | 0 | 1 | 2 | 3 | 4 | 5 | 6 | 7 | 8 | 9 | 10 |
| touch | 0 | 1 | 2 | 3 | 4 | 5 | 6 | 7 | 8 | 9 | 10 |
| taste | 0 | 1 | 2 | 3 | 4 | 5 | 6 | 7 | 8 | 9 | 10 |
| _____ | 0 | 1 | 2 | 3 | 4 | 5 | 6 | 7 | 8 | 9 | 10 |
| _____ | 0 | 1 | 2 | 3 | 4 | 5 | 6 | 7 | 8 | 9 | 10 |

**Affective/Social Aspects**

| cooperation | 0 | 1 | 2 | 3 | 4 | 5 | 6 | 7 | 8 | 9 | 10 |
| enthusiasm | 0 | 1 | 2 | 3 | 4 | 5 | 6 | 7 | 8 | 9 | 10 |
| non-verbal interaction | 0 | 1 | 2 | 3 | 4 | 5 | 6 | 7 | 8 | 9 | 10 |
| conversation | 0 | 1 | 2 | 3 | 4 | 5 | 6 | 7 | 8 | 9 | 10 |
| physical contact | 0 | 1 | 2 | 3 | 4 | 5 | 6 | 7 | 8 | 9 | 10 |
| participation | 0 | 1 | 2 | 3 | 4 | 5 | 6 | 7 | 8 | 9 | 10 |
| emotional response | 0 | 1 | 2 | 3 | 4 | 5 | 6 | 7 | 8 | 9 | 10 |
| even disposition | 0 | 1 | 2 | 3 | 4 | 5 | 6 | 7 | 8 | 9 | 10 |
| competition | 0 | 1 | 2 | 3 | 4 | 5 | 6 | 7 | 8 | 9 | 10 |
| task completion | 0 | 1 | 2 | 3 | 4 | 5 | 6 | 7 | 8 | 9 | 10 |
| range of interests | 0 | 1 | 2 | 3 | 4 | 5 | 6 | 7 | 8 | 9 | 10 |
| _____ | 0 | 1 | 2 | 3 | 4 | 5 | 6 | 7 | 8 | 9 | 10 |
| _____ | 0 | 1 | 2 | 3 | 4 | 5 | 6 | 7 | 8 | 9 | 10 |

**Figure 2**   Staff Observation Scale

whose life revolved around baseball may enjoy playing whiffleball or using a Nerf™ ball with a short/fat bat.  Taking the clients to local games may be almost as positive an experience as actually playing.

It is important to find out why they liked the activity in which they engaged on a regular basis.  It may have been for socialization, so another activity might serve the same purpose.  For example, the lady who liked to quilt may find the baking group provides the socialization she needs.

People participate in activities for a variety of reasons.  These may include;  a sense of challenge, a sense of accomplishment, socialization, increasing self-esteem, and enjoying the competition.  There is always a motivation behind why the person engages in an activity.  It is not always possible for people to verbalize why they participate, but an interest indicator can help determine the client's reasons for participation.

It is important to determine the subtle difference between whether to modify the familiar activity or to find a new program which provides a similar feeling to that of the old activity.

The old activity may no longer be of interest to clients because they can not do it to an acceptable level of performance, or because they are tired of it.  An example of this is the many arts and crafts specialists who have indicated they do not want to engage in any crafts when they are older.  All of these little factors need to be ascertained if a leisure interest survey is to be useful.

## Interest Survey Format

The interest inventory format should be simplified with a series of checklists so it will be easily administered and used as quick reference.  If the client is capable of filling out the indicator form without assistance this should be encouraged.  Encouraging clients to function independently helps to meet the goal of functioning to the best of their abilities.  It is imperative that this goal remains in the staff's thinking at all times.  Some clients may need assistance to complete the survey, while in other cases the staff may have to use a combination of client verbal responses and family information.

A leisure interest indicator should include the following types of questions in the Leisure Interest Survey [Figure 3] on page 12.

## Activity Analysis

Before the goal planning process can occur, the staff should review the potential activity offerings to determine what physical, social/affective and cognitive characteristics are inherent within each activity.  This process of reviewing activities was developed by Peterson and Gunn (1984 p. 180).  They state, "activity analysis is a procedure for breaking down and examining an activity to find the inherent characteristics that contribute to program objectives." Their procedure is comprehensive and extremely detailed, making it somewhat cumbersome to use in the limited time available to the recreation staff.

## Leisure Interest Survey

Do you prefer to spend your free time:
>    alone    with friends    with others    I don't know

My favorite time of year is:
>    spring    summer    fall    winter

>    I like it because_____.

My favorite time of day is:
>    morning    afternoon    evening

>    I like it because_____.

I am busiest on:
>    Monday    Tuesday    Wednesday    Thursday    Friday    Saturday    Sunday

I am sometimes bored on:
>    Monday    Tuesday    Wednesday    Thursday    Friday    Saturday    Sunday

When I have free time I like to:

_____,

because_____.

Places I prefer to do things:
>    in the facility              off the floor
>    in my room                outdoors
>    in the lounge              away from the facility

When I do an activity, I prefer to do things:
>    physical-using my arms/hands      working with animals/plants
>    physical-using my legs              artistic activities
>    reading/writing                        religious programs
>    with numbers

What is one activity you did when you were younger that you would like to do again?

_____.

Name one current activity you would like to continue doing?

_____.

What activity do you do that takes a lot of energy?

_____.

What activity do you do that relaxes you?

_____.

Do you have an activity you would like to do that you have never had the opportunity to do before?

_____.

Check the activities you would be interested in observing or participating in:

>    __ games          __ art/music        __ outdoor          __ religious
>    __ exercise       __ service          __ collecting
>    __ crafts         __ sports           __ entertainment

**Figure 3**  Leisure Interest Survey Form

The following Activity Analysis [Figure 4, pp. 14-15] form, based on the work of Peterson and Gunn (1984) has been developed to provide a simple though effective method for the busy activity leader to document the inherent values of the recreation activities.

Each activity is reviewed by looking at individual characteristics which fall under the physical, social/affective or cognitive categories. To be consistent all of the characteristics are evaluated, even if one does not apply to the specific activity. A mark (x) is placed in the "none" category if the characteristic does not apply to this particular activity. For example, bingo involves very little range of motion with the arms; therefore, a mark would be placed in the "none" category. On the other hand, bowling would receive a higher mark along the scale for range of motion.

The staff review the activity by placing marks along the continuum, rating each characteristic on how the activity comments section is supplied so the staff member can make notations of possible modifications for a specific client or condition. The end result is a profile of the activity showing the strengths of that particular activity.

This profile can assist the staff in many ways, the first of which is to encourage the client to attend programs whose characteristics are the same as the client's needs. For example, a client may need to adjust to life in the nursing home. This client might traditionally be encouraged to attend familiar programs such as bingo and crafts. After completing the activity analysis form, the staff discover bingo has little to no socialization/verbalization involved. This may be a very poor choice for the client who needs to be meeting the other people in the facility. Crafts, the other familiar activity, has greater potential for socialization and, an end product is produced. This may be a frightening thought for the new client who is fearful that his or her project will not be as good as the other clients. A drop-in coffee hour or a gardening program may end up being better activities for the client who needs to adjust to the facility.

The information obtained in the activity analysis process assists the staff to make informed decisions about activity selection when dealing with client's needs and interests in treatment planning meetings. The terminology taken from the activity analysis form can aid the recreation staff member when searching for the proper wording in goal development and in dealings with other professionals.

## Program Analysis

The next step in the activity analysis process is to compare and contrast all of the activity offerings against each other. This profile, of all of the activities, shows the staff which components and senses have been under- and overutilized [see Figure 5, p. 16].

For example, one facility discovered every activity required the sense of sight, yet only two programs utilized the sense of smell. They were able to modify the program offerings to include a better balance of activities for all of the senses. Another agency determined that most of their program offerings used only the upper body. They changed their program to include more walking and bending and stooping opportunities.

New activity ideas should be analyzed prior to implementation to make sure they compliment the current offerings. Programs which would expand the characteristics would be offered prior to those which would continue to meet the same needs.

Activity analysis has many uses within the facility. The time spent completing and analyzing the activity offerings assists in the provision of a well-rounded, client-oriented recreation program.

## Recreation Activity Analysis

Activity: _____ Rater: _____

Description: _____

_____

### Physical Aspects

Comments:

Body Movements: _____
      sedentary            bending/stooping

Arms/Hands—Range of Motion: _____
      little            full

    Dexterity: _____
      little (reading)      great (sketching)

    Lifting: _____
      light (pencils)      heavy (bowling ball)

Legs/Feet—Joint Motion: _____
      none         much (steps, curbs)

    Flexibility: _____
      little (walking)      much (stooping/kicking)

Coordination—Body Parts: _____
      none         precise

    Hand/Eye: _____
      none         precise

Endurance: _____
      little         much

### Cognitive Aspects

Concentration: _____
      none         great

Memory Retention: _____
      short term      long term

Verbalization: _____
      none (nonverbal response)      much (creative thought)

Skill level: _____
      low (ball toss)      high (reading, computation)

**Figure 4**   Recreation Activity Analysis

Sensory Discrimination:                                                    **Comments:**

      Sight:            _____
                low                      high

      Smell:            _____
                low                      high

      Touch:            _____
                low                      high

      Hearing:          _____
                low                      high

      Taste:            _____
                low                      high

### Affective/Social Aspects

Interaction:           _____
                low                      high

Physical Contact:      _____
                low                      high

Competition:           _____
                low                      high

Emotional Response:    _____
                low                      high

**Figure 4** (Continued)   Recreation Activity Analysis

| Activity | | | | | | | | | | | | |
|---|---|---|---|---|---|---|---|---|---|---|---|---|
| **Physical Aspects** | | | | | | | | | | | | |
| bending | | | | | | | | | | | | |
| range of motion-ROM | | | | | | | | | | | | |
| dexterity | | | | | | | | | | | | |
| lifting | | | | | | | | | | | | |
| leg/feet | | | | | | | | | | | | |
| flexibility | | | | | | | | | | | | |
| coordination of body parts | | | | | | | | | | | | |
| hand/eye coordination | | | | | | | | | | | | |
| endurance | | | | | | | | | | | | |
| **Cognitive Aspects** | | | | | | | | | | | | |
| concentration | | | | | | | | | | | | |
| memory retention | | | | | | | | | | | | |
| verbalization | | | | | | | | | | | | |
| skill level | | | | | | | | | | | | |
| sensory sight | | | | | | | | | | | | |
| smell | | | | | | | | | | | | |
| touch | | | | | | | | | | | | |
| hearing | | | | | | | | | | | | |
| taste | | | | | | | | | | | | |
| **Affective/Social Aspects** | | | | | | | | | | | | |
| interaction | | | | | | | | | | | | |
| physical contact | | | | | | | | | | | | |
| competition | | | | | | | | | | | | |
| emotional response | | | | | | | | | | | | |

0 = None; 1 = Very Low or Little; 3 = Intermediate or Medium; 5 = Very High or Very Much

**Figure 5** Program Analysis

## Summary

Client assessment is the first step in providing a quality program which is client-oriented. The client assessment, in combination with the results from an interest indicator, provides a profile of the client's strengths, needs, and interests. This profile will be utilized in the goal development process which is outlined in Chapter 3. However, before appropriate goals can be determined for the client, the staff should have analyzed the potential activity offerings in their quest to provide a quality program. A comparison of the various program offerings in terms of inherent benefits promotes a holistic approach to recreation programming.

## Resources

American Health Care Association. (1989). *The Long Term Care Survey.* Washington DC: AHCA

*Before the Surveyor Knocks: Preparing for the New OBRA Survey.* Washington, DC: AAHA Publications.

*The Long Term Care Survey Newsletter.* Baltimore, MD: Health Professions Press.

O'Morrow, G. (1980). *Therapeutic Recreation: A Helping Profession.* Reston, VA: Reston Publishing.

Peterson, C. A. (1978). *Characteristics of Special Populations.* Washington, DC: Hawkins and Associates, Inc.

Peterson, C. A. and Gunn, S. L. (1984). *Therapeutic Recreation Program Design.* Englewood Cliffs, NJ: Prentice-Hall, Inc.

Peterson, C. A. and Gunn, S. L. (1984). *Therapeutic Recreation Program Design: Principles and Procedures.* Englewood, NJ: Prentice-Hall, Inc.

## NOTES

# CHAPTER 3

# DOCUMENTATION

Goal Planning

Components Of An Objective

Writing Client-Oriented Objectives

Progress Notes

Summary

Resources

# DOCUMENTATION

Documentation involves two components; first goal development and second progress notations. Documentation is the road map of the clients' situation within the facility. Documentation is the staff's way of being able to communicate with each other. Many professionals would say that if it is not written down in the goal statements or progress notes, the behavior does not exist. Documentation has become vital in the quality care chain.

Each client deserves to have the goals written for his/her specific situation. The days are gone when each client had the same goal of "increased socialization" or "adjustment to the facility." Although both of the above may be appropriate goals for some clients they are not for everyone. Each client deserves, and is required by law, to be treated as an individual, no matter how large or small the facility.

At this point, a client assessment has been completed as well as an interest indicator and the staff has spent some time with the client. Also, the recreation staff has an understanding of the inherent benefits within the recreation activities which they are capable of scheduling at the facility.

The various disciplines begin developing a series of goal statements for the client after the initial completion of the assessment and interest indicator. In many instances, this takes place in an inter-disciplinary setting with the client participating. In order to receive Medicare and Medicaid funding, regulations become more stringent, and the importance of good assessment, the team approach, and goal development become a requirement for Minimal Standards regulations. The team needs work together to develop the goals based upon the clients' functioning level, utilizing recreation as one of the tools to reach the goals. The team, working together, may be assisting the client to adjust to the facility or to make simple decisions. Everyone is aware of the goal and work within each specialty to assist the client. This is particularly appropriate with goals dealing with behavior problems. For example, the client may strike out at the staff. The goal may be for the client to refrain from striking out for a certain period of time. Each discipline then works at meeting that goal.

Utilizing the team approach, behavior based goals are easier to remember, to accomplish, and are of more value to the client than activity based goals. Although activity-based goals such as "the client is requested to attend the sing-a-long" have their place, it is more appropriate that the team approach focuses on the entire person.

Most facilities are moving toward this integrated approach to goal development in order to meet current regulation. It is time for recreation professionals to join the team and show that they have an important contribution to make.

The following materials on goal development are to assist the recreation professional be a vital part of the treatment team.


## Goal Planning

*Goals are broad statements of intent.* They state what will be accomplished. Goals are generally written in somewhat vague terms and may or may not include a possible deadline. They can be of a short-term or long-term nature. They may be reachable within a few days or not for a longer time period, such as six months. Remembering that the clients are older adults, even long-term goals should be realistic, such as a six month period versus a year. For example, "the client will identify his room" is a short term goal, but this is still a vague statement of what is hoped to be accomplished. "The client will adjust to the nursing home" is certainly a vague statement of intent. There are no steps listed that indicate how this will be reached. Again a date could be indicated such as "within six weeks," but the goal still remains rather long-term and vague.

*Goal statements establish intent as well as a sense of direction.* They are imperative when establishing documentation on the client. However, because of the vague nature of goals, it may be difficult to know when the goal has been reached. This is where objectives enter the picture. *Objectives (short term goals) are the specific, measurable steps one will take in order to meet the goal.*

Many facilities and recreation professionals write a long-term goal and then utilize a series of short-term goals as objectives to reach the longer term goal. There is nothing wrong with this approach as long as the short-term goals meet the same criteria as an objective.

Goals and objectives can be written for any of the three domains—physical, cognitive, or social/affective. An increase in attention span would fall under the cognitive domain. Feeding oneself, or taking a daily walk would be under the physical domain. Although it is possible to establish a goal for the client in each domain, the most pressing need should be established first.

## Components Of An Objective

After the goal is developed and the domain it falls under established, it is important to establish the steps which will take place to meet the goal or goals. *An objective has three components –an action, criteria, and conditions.* Each of the individual components will be covered in the following section.

### Action

The first is the *Action or Performance.* Every objective must have some visible action that can be observed. It is easiest to see objectives which are physical. The staff can observe when a person walks or lifts his/her arm. Cognitive objectives are often the most difficult to observe as they usually involve understanding. The staff may have a tendency to write "The client will listen to the music" or "The client will know the rules of bocci ball," yet neither of those statements are observable. So, the first component of an objective is that it has an action or performance which can be observed. There are words which will help make a cognitive objective observable. They include the following: list, teach, discuss, write, recite, verbalize, state, demonstrate. They should replace such words as "understand," "know," and "listen" because it is impossible to determine if someone is actually listening. The same can be said for "know." The only way the staff can tell if someone knows the rules of the game is to ask the person to "recite," "list," or "write" the rules.

## Criteria

Now that the first component of an objective has been identified, the second component of an objective is the *Criteria*. Without some way to measure whether or not the objective has been met, it is impossible to determine success. Usually criteria is determined by one of the following: *the number of or percentage of times the action is completed or the length of time the action is done*. For example, "the client will roll the ball to the therapist at least three times during the session." An example of using criteria as a percentage would be "fifty percent of the time, the client will open her eyes when addressed by name." To use time as criteria, "the client will discuss gardening techniques for at least five minutes with the therapist." Criteria is crucial in any objective. Without criteria there is no method for measuring success. The criteria lists the standard performance which will be acceptable.

Every objective must have some minimal criteria level. However, any objective can be made stronger by combining criteria. For example, a combination of number of times and a time frame within which the behavior will occur gives a more accurate picture of the performance. Using the example of the client who was to roll the ball three times, he could perform this action in succession within a few seconds or it may take an hour. With the way the objective is currently written either one would be acceptable. If the desired behavior is to roll the ball quickly then time should be added into the criteria: "Within five minutes, the client will roll the ball to the therapist three times." The client can also be asked to perform the action every single time requested. Words such as "everytime," "always," "all" are acceptable criteria however, it is often difficult to achieve an objective to such a level.

## Conditions

The third component *Conditions*, make objectives easier to understand; however, they are not required in order to be a measurable objective. Conditions help make it easier for another reader to understand what is to be accomplished. Conditions are the things given to the client in order to meet the objective. For example, "after six weeks of instruction, the client will find his/her own room every time without any instructions from the staff." Or, "given the needles, yarn and instructions the client will crochet a scarf with no errors." Words such as "with," "within," "given" usually indicate the conditions. As noted earlier, it is not always necessary to state the conditions. Some agencies may have a section on the documentation known as "method" which could be considered the same as the conditions.

## Writing Client-Oriented Objectives

When writing objectives, it is important to constantly remember it is the client who is doing the action and not the staff member. A common inappropriate objective written from the staff point of view is "the staff will play music for the client three times a week." Even though it is often difficult to write client oriented objectives, it is not an objective unless the client does the action. An easy way to avoid this pitfall of objective writing is to always start the statement with the client's name. For example, "Mrs. Smith will open her eyes every time she is addressed by name." It becomes clear that Mrs. Smith is to do the action instead of the staff member.

## Keeping Objectives Concise

Objectives should always be short, simple statements of intent. If the statement has the word "and" in the portion of the objective, it is two objectives. For example, "the client will open her eyes and smile whenever she is presented with sensory stimulation materials," is really two different actions. The first is to open her eyes and the second is to smile. Since smiling is a more complex movement than opening the eyes, the first objective would be to get the client to open her eyes consistently. Whenever that has been accomplished, smiling should be introduced. If the need is there to write two objectives then do so, but it becomes difficult to work on more than one or two objectives at any one point in time. *Objectives should be kept simple with only one action per objective.*

## Objectives for Lower-Functioning Clients

Often the frustration of objective development is writing for the lower functioning client. There is a tendency to write objectives which are too vague to measure. For example, "the client will respond to sensory stimulation activities" is so broad, a therapist would have difficulty noting achievement. A specific action such as "open her eyes," "follow with his eyes," "turn her head," "squeeze the therapist's hands," or " smile," is much easier to observe and measure. Some measurement of success such as "at least once during a session," "for ten seconds" or, "fifty percent of the time," must be included even when writing objectives for lower level clients.

A specific action in combination with a measurement makes objective writing for lower level clients easier to manage as well as more realistic. The conditions surrounding the desired action are especially helpful when writing objectives for lower functioning clients. Conditions allow the staff to indicate the type of activity they will utilize as well as the time frame before a behavior change is expected. For example, "after three weeks of daily visits with sensory activities, the client will open her eyes at least once each session." This objective provides the staff with a sense of direction as well as a specific action and criteria to measure. Writing objectives for the lower level client can be a rewarding experience and certainly one in which the entire team of professionals should participate.

## Objectives for Higher-Functioning Clients

Once in a great while, a client will have met every possible goal and there is a tendency to write, "This client will maintain her high level of functioning." If this is the case, then the client probably could be discharged from the nursing home. If the client is participating to a high level in recreation activities, yet continues to need nursing home care, a leadership goal might be established, but expanded treatment objectives must meet all regulations. The client might deliver mail, act as a greeter to new clients, conduct a portion of an activity, read announcements over the intercom system, or develop articles for the client newspaper. It takes imagination and conversation with the client to determine what the next step should be for that individual.

## Progress Notes

After the objectives are written, notes about the client's progress are made referring back to the objectives. Notes should always be made on observations and not on the professional's conjecture. For example, it is inappropriate for a recreation professional to state that a client "seems depressed." The recreation professional should outline observations such as: "client would not look at the therapist"; "client sat in chair and stared out the window"; or "client exhibited no response to conversation." These statements are the observations which might lead a professional to an assumption of depression, but the cause could be something else entirely. Therefore, only write what is observed not what is guessed. Progress notes always refer back to the goals and objectives at some point in the narrative. If there is no reference to the goals and objectives, another person reading the notes would be unable to tell whether or not the goals and objectives were feasible and being met. It is acceptable to revise goals and objectives when writing progress notes. If the objective hasn't been achieved, but is still possible, then leave it the same. Make a notation as to why it has been left the same. If the objective is not feasible, develop a new objective. *Always make a statement referring to the goals and objectives when writing progress notes.; if dropped or changed, include a statement why.*

How often progress notes are written depends on the current regulations However, any time there is a significant change in a client's functioning level, notes are to be written. This may mean notes are written once a week or more often depending on the client's condition.

Documentation, which includes goal development and progress notes, is the written profile of the client. It must be approached in a positive manner by the team of care givers because it is the written plan which establishes a sense of direction for each individual client.

## Summary

The recreation personnel must approach documentation in a professional manner as a part of the team. The goals should be statements of intent with well-written objectives being the steps to meet the goals. Objectives have the client performing an observable action which is measurable by an agreed upon set of criteria. Progress notes are notations of observed behaviors and not conjectures on the staff's part. Notations are clear, concise and refer to the goals and objectives. If the staff approach documentation in this manner, the task will not appear so overwhelming.

## Resources

*Documentation in Long Term Care.* (1989). Alexandria, VA: NRPA Publications.

Mager, R. F. (1962). *Preparing Instructional Objectives.* Belmont, CA: Lear Siegler/Fearon Publications

Sauder, P. *Activity Care Plans for Long-Term Care Facilities.* Houston, TX: Mand H. Publishing Co.

# CLIENT MOTIVATION AND PARTICIPATION

# CLIENT MOTIVATION AND PARTICIPATION

One of the most common concerns expressed by recreation professionals is the lack of motivation many of the clients exhibit toward recreation programming. In many instances, the clients seem motivated to do little except eat and sit in their rooms. It must be remembered that clients do have a choice as to whether or not to attend recreation programming and many of the supposedly "unmotivated" clients are simply taking advantage of this choice. Clients residing in a nursing home must wake up and get dressed at a specified time. They must eat their meals and take showers and in many instances attend various types of therapy. The fact that recreation is optional means that they have the right to refuse all activity, thus exercising control on one aspect of their life. Recreational activities can no longer only be scheduled at staff convenience.

## Avoidance—A Natural Reaction

At times, it seem clients are not actually unmotivated, but rather motivated not to attend. They often have very creative reasons for not attending. They seem to go out of their way to avoid attending recreation programming. The following section will explore just a few of the reasons clients often appear motivated not to attend activities. Hopefully by identifying some of the causes for unmotivated behavior, possible solutions will present themselves as well.

Whenever a client is invited to an activity he has three possible options. *The first one is to avoid the experience.* Everyone has some activity they would rather avoid than do in front of other people. It may involve heights and the person is afraid of heights; he will do almost anything to avoid that experience. "But, the clients won't be involved with anything that challenging or dangerous" is what the professional is saying at this point. Remember that what is not too frustrating, embarrassing or challenging to the staff may be an extremely fearful experience for the client. A previous unpleasant experience with a similar activity is enough to keep the person from attending. The thought of being embarrassed because they are overweight, incontinent, don't have teeth or full usage of a body part are just a few of the examples as to why clients may wish to avoid an experience.

The thought that they may do poorly at the activity always enters into the picture. And everyone at some point is afraid of being seen as foolish. The client may not like to feel they are stupid. But a recreation professional at this point is saying, "that would never happen." Again, what is embarrassing to one person is certainly not the same as it is to someone else. Even though the staff want to be reassuring and comforting the risk from the client's point of view may be that this experience is too difficult, therefore to be avoided.

For example, as a younger person, the client went bowling. The ball became stuck in the gutter and had to be retrieved by the client. Whenever she is asked to go bowling now, she remembers that experience and refuses to attend. Another client will not do crafts in the craft room because her work is not as good as the craft assistant who keeps telling her it will get better with practice.

Some of the most successful programs show the recreation professionals as people who can laugh at themselves as they make mistakes. The craft assistant whose picture is just a bit off-center too, or the recreation leader who has trouble hitting the ball, helps to ease the fears and concerns of clients. Finding out the client's reasoning behind the refusal to attend and presenting reassurance can do a lot to ease the fears about trying a new activity which could be potentially embarrassing. The recreation professional must constantly remember the clients' fears and concerns when they are attending a program.

## Observation—The Initial Step

The second option the client has in any experience is to *observe without actually participating*. Recreation professionals make a mistake when they insist that everyone jump right in and get involved. Especially if the activity is a new experience for the client, it may be highly desirable for the client to observe it first. If the option to observe is not available, naturally passive clients may select avoidance. That would be easier and less embarrassing than participating in an activity in which the client may not be successful. Remember, it is the client's thinking that makes the difference in participation. The staff may say everyone will be successful at the experience, but if the client has a feeling of having done better, he/she may become embarrassed and avoid further participation. The solution is quite easy. If a client is avoiding an experience and the recreation professional can reassure the client that he can observe, he has made a step in the direction of participation. If a client will attend and observe, but not participate, be patient. It is conceivable that with a little time and support from the staff, this client will soon be an active participant.

## Participation—Positive Reinforcement

*The last possible option is participation.* It is wonderful when clients readily participate in recreation experiences, but even those who do participate may be selective in terms of the types of activities they choose. Positive reinforcement is necessary for every client.

The use of an interest indicator, found in Chapter 2, can assist the staff in determining the level of readiness for each individual client. Knowing the best time of day and day of week for each client in terms of participation will assist the programmer in moving clients from avoidance to active participation.

Even after identifying that clients are avoiding recreation programming and why, it may not be enough to get them out of their rooms. Many of the clients are afraid that if they leave the room, their things will either be stolen or moved to another room. In the past, when clients did leave, it was not uncommon for room changes to take place; their fears are not unfounded. Also their rooms are safe. It is where their possessions are and therefore, a comfortable environment. Especially if the client is new to the facility, this feeling of security is justified.

The obvious solution is to establish a rapport with the client. But even that may not be enough to get the client out of the room. Taking activities and small groups with similar interests to the client's room helps to make the transition from "motivated not to attend" to becoming an active participant. A soap opera club or the baseball group can easily meet in a client's room to watch the program. A volunteer might co-ordinate a current event or discussion group which meets in the client's room on a regular basis. The client will be more comfortable in his/her own room and the added motivation from the others can be helpful in getting the client to attend activities outside of the room. The special group can arrange for an outing or special meeting which takes place outside of the client's room once the group gets established.

Sometimes clients are motivated not to attend because the staff are asking them to participate in a new experience. This certainly loops back to the idea of avoiding a new and potentially embarrassing situation. Some clients do not participate because they have never engaged in recreational activities and are afraid to start now. Often clients expend a great deal of energy to avoid participation in activities.

Staff often encourage the clients to participate in an activity with people they do not know or, in some cases, with people they do not like. There is a tendency to avoid being around clients who are functioning at a lower level than themselves. It seems to be too much of a reminder that someday they too could require additional care. Although separate activities for all occasions is not recommended, some activities where higher functioning level clients can participate together should be scheduled.

## Phases Of The Recreation Experience

Every recreation experience involves a series of phases which can affect client motivation. If a negative experience occurs during one of these phases the client may decide not to participate in the future. *The phases are: (a) anticipation, (b) travel to, (c) the activity, (d) travel from, and (e) recall.* The recreation professional may have little or not control over several of these phases, yet it is the uncontrolled aspects which may be affecting client motivation.

During the first phase, *anticipation*, the client often considers the experience before it takes place and creates a negative scenario which affects his/her attendance. For example, a male client has agreed to go on an outing into the community. However, between the sign-up date and the actual experience the client begins to think about the possibility that there may not be a bathroom when he needs one. The client decides it is safer not to attend. The same can be said for an activity which will take place at home. The client may decide he doesn't care for a crowd. He anticipates a crowded room and decides not to attend based upon his anticipation of the experience. The recreation staff can only turn this type of thinking around when they figure out what negative scenario the client has created. Providing positive information about specific concerns is better than a vague reassurance that everything will be fine. This might mean telling the clients how close their seats will be to the restroom, assuring them that they will have their own volunteers or promising to save a seat by the door for a particular client. Whatever the concern, the reassurances that the staff provide must insure that the client's fears are unfounded. The staff must uphold any promises made during this discussion.

The recreation staff can assist the client to have a positive anticipation phase at large events by encouraging them to help prepare decorations and baking goodies for the event. Discussion groups or games may also help prepare the clients. Before taking the clients to a large county fair, the staff of one facility play the game *The Price is Right* to help prepare clients for the prices they might expect. The clients remembered when a sandwich was fifty cents so the game helps to prepare them for the current cost. Select activities that will assist the clients to have a positive anticipation phase as well as add onto the variety of recreation programming being offered.

The second phase of the recreation experience is *travel*. Unless the activity is conducted in the client's room there is going to be a travel phase. The travel phase may only be down the hall to a lounge, but even this short trip can affect the experience. If the client is pushed too fast, shoved into an elevator backward, or is assisted by a staff member who talks as if the client is not even present, the client may decide never to attend again. Having to wait too long before an activity begins may also affect the travel phase. Staff must remember that clients must be treated with dignity at all times. Staff and volunteers should be reminded on a regular basis of the proper methods for transporting clients. Role playing with the staff or volunteers acting as clients is an excellent method for demonstrating how the clients must feel when they are treated without dignity.

At times, the staff have no actual control over the experience until the client reaches the *actual activity*. In many instances the client enjoys the activity but has had so many concerns with the other phases that he does not wish to attend. Many factors can influence the client's experience at the actual experience. The inability to see the action from where the client is sitting; being disturbed by another client; not getting enough food; feeling too crowded; having to wait; or being inappropriately dressed are only a few of the factors which can affect attendance.

Clients are generally very understanding of, and often highly entertained by, the mistakes the staff make in providing the program. However, if the mistakes directly influence their personal comfort, they are not as easily forgotten. Staff should always be aware of the client's individual needs and comforts and remember this is the phase over which the staff has the control.

*The return travel phase* can make a difference in further attendance. The clients may have enjoyed the experience very much, but may have had to wait too long to be returned to their rooms. Or, the bus trip back was too long or too late in the evening for them. Staff should have a method to obtain extra client transport assistance after a large program. Possibly a call to the nursing unit or the recreation department five minutes prior to the end of the event in order to obtain extra transport assistance would make the difference in how the clients evaluated the total experience. Taking short bus trips with a travel time of less than one hour with a rest stop for a snack may alleviate the travel concerns when on an outing away from the facility.

The last phase of the experience is *recall*. Again the recreation personnel often have little control over this phase. However, the staff can assist the client to recall a happy experience. Helping clients write articles for the newspaper, holding discussion groups, or showing slides/photos of the event can make this phase more positive. Mementos such as badges, ribbons or certificates can also help other staff members assist with the recall phase by asking the clients about their experiences as they go about their daily routine.

## Traditional Program Concerns

The recreation staff should be responsible for all client recreation programming within the facility. The schedule is compiled on a weekly and monthly basis with a variety of special events which occur on a regular or seasonal basis. Often the staff schedule programs with little regard to the amount of time that should be devoted to individualized programming, small group activities and for larger groups or clients.

The schedule often reflects staff interests rather than the needs and interests of the clientele. Many schedules show little change from week to week or month to month. Activities are scheduled based upon the premise that there should be mostly small group activities with a few special events and some individualized activities thrown in to vary the program.

Unfortunately, this approach to programming results in a rather small percentage of clients attending recreation programming on a regular basis. An analysis of these traditional program schedules, in terms of the attendance and the types of programs offered, usually reveals that the programs are reaching only five percent of the clients.

Many of the clients are functioning on such a level that they require 1:1 attention from the recreation professionals. The shear numbers of clients needing this specialized attention often outweighs the number of hours which are available for such activity within the daily schedule. On the other hand, many clients are willing, able, and interested in participating in group activities. These clients often receive the bulk of the programming efforts.

# Levels Of Participation

This section is designed to look at the clients' level of functioning in terms of their readiness and ability to participate in group programming. It is not meant to label the clients into rigid categories. Rather, it is meant to provide a realistic basis for determining how programming efforts should be distributed to meet the programming needs of all levels. For example, if most of the present recreation schedule is small group programs, but most of the clients need one-on-one attention, the program is unbalanced.

Determining what percentage of clients are functioning at what participation level is the first step in scheduling a balanced program. This gives a basis for determining how much of an effort should be placed on 1:1 activities, small group programs and large group special programs.

Five participation levels have been identified. They may be combined or modified to meet the needs of a particular situation. The participation levels are based solely on whether or not the client is able to participate in group activities so the staff can determine how much programming of each type should be provided. The levels are based upon mental capacities rather than physical abilities such as hearing, ambulation and eyesight.

## No Verbal Response

This is the client who usually remains in bed or sits in a chair by the bed. Occasionally the staff may take this individual to a day room or lounge. No verbal response, or very little, is exhibited that is based in reality. The client appears to be disoriented in both time and place and seems to have withdrawn into his/her own world. If the person is taken to recreation activities, the staff can not tell if anything is being absorbed. The client often sleeps during group activities or simply exhibits no response to the program. The best approach for any type of response is to work on a 1:1 basis in the client's room where the staff member can concentrate on stimulating a positive response.

Although each person must be seen as an individual with as much time being spent with the individual as needed, it becomes important to develop a time frame for scheduling 1:1 visits for a few clients may be able to tolerate slightly longer visits than others. Five minutes can seem like an eternity to a therapist, but it may take that long for the person to realize there is someone in the room with them. On the other hand, if the visit is too long, the client becomes overly tired.

It is desirable for those people functioning on this 1:1 level to be visited daily. However, with more clients functioning at this level, this becomes an impossible task without additional staff. Short visits of five to ten minutes at least three times a week, should be considered a minimum amount of time to spend with the lowest level client. Suggested activities for these visits will be discussed later.

## Unable to Attend Group Programming

The client who functions at this level is usually somewhat confused and/or disoriented. This may be the person who wanders away during a program or who constantly bangs on the table top. Actions are often exhibited which irritate the other members of the group. Teeth grinding, mumbling, or screaming are examples. Verbal responses are sometimes given, but when he/she attends a group program so much intensive staff attention is required that the rest of the group suffers. This client can easily become over-stimulated in a group atmosphere and should be observed for signs of fatigue. When possible, such clients should be encouraged to participate in some group programming because of the added stimuli from other clients, however, this person will need individualized attention in addition to the group experience.

Several 1:1 sessions are required each week for this functioning level, supplemented with group programming, when feasible. At least one hour of programming on an individualized basis should be scheduled per week. This time should be broken into small increments so the client does not become over-stimulated.

## Capable But Motivated Not to Attend

In terms of client levels, this group is certainly the most challenging. These are the people who are capable of attending group activities, but select not to attend. They usually spend a great deal of time in their own room. If the client is actively involved with personal pursuits and family, the recreation professionals' concern would be lessened. However, they usually sit alone and do not interact well with other clients.

Often labeled "unmotivated," these clients avoid group experiences and create a variety of excuses for not attending. A closer look at these clients reveal that they are actually very motivated not to get involved.

The initial step to involving this client in group activity is the building of a trusting relationship with the therapist. Short 1:1 sessions in a comfortable area should be scheduled for a total of one hour per week until this rapport is established. A good volunteer may be able to supplement the staff visits. This person is usually starved for attention and affection, but is reluctant to leave the safety of his/her room. The staff need to develop creative ways to draw this person into the mainstream of facility life. Going in to talk three times a week may be sufficient to involve the person in group activities outside the room, but there is often a need to take another client or two along to interact. Attention from volunteers and other clients can greatly reduce the amount of staff time necessary to move this person to a different level of participation. The section of *Client Motivation* has additional information for working with this client.

## Selective

This client is usually capable of deciding what recreation activities he or she would like to pursue and will do so on a selective basis. An example of this is the lady who only attends bingo and church services. She has very narrow interests and needs staff encouragement in order to attend more than two activities.

The activities this type of client pursues are usually very familiar and therefore very safe. The staff's role is to be supportive and to encourage new experiences. Special events and outings are often the way to involve this client in a broader range of experiences.

If this client is so selective that program attendance is less than once a week, consider the client as *Motivated Not To Attend*. This person is often afraid to try new activities. Assigning a volunteer to attend specific activities with this client often increases participation. Efforts should be made to introduce clients with similar interests to each other at these events.

## Motivated

This is the type of client most recreation professionals would like to see residing at the facility. They actually fall into two categories, the first being the client who is motivated to initiate his/her own experiences and attends a wide variety of scheduled programs several times a week. In the other category is the client who greets the recreation professional eagerly every day awaiting to be assigned to some activity. It doesn't seem to matter what activity is offered, this person will be there, however he/she is not yet capable of initiating activities. Often the motivated clients are the bulk of the clients the staff sees within a facility. However, with encouragement some of the *Selective* and *Motivated Not To Attend* clients can move into this category.

Even the clients who function in the *Motivated* category should be encouraged to meet other clients and initiate experiences with them. Teaching them activities and skills they can do on their own and introducing them to clients with similar interests are the first steps toward client initiated activities. Encouraging them to make decisions and invite friends to events are a part of this process. Interest indicators identify appropriate activities for a starting place (see Chapter 2).

These clients may need specialized leisure education sessions as a part of their regular recreation experiences. They should have at least one experience daily. Highly trained volunteers can supplement the recreation programming efforts.

The staff is cautioned to remember this group represents only a small percentage of the clientele, yet most of the programming efforts are often aimed toward these motivated clients.

## The Program Dilemma

A determination of how many clients function at each level is meant to provide a guideline for staff in terms of program time allocation. If most of the clients require 1:1 attention, an elaborate small group schedule would be inappropriate. On the other hand, group activities and special events are an important part of the programming. It is only through these types of programming that social interaction can occur.

Additional staff seems to be the answer, but creative scheduling of the current staff can solve much of the programming dilemma. Individual 1:1 sessions could be scheduled during "down" group programming times such as early morning, right before and after meals and during change of shift.  Even though the nursing personnel may be especially busy during the above mentioned times, there will still be clients who are available for a short 1:1 session.  A combination of 1:1 activity sessions interspersed with group sessions helps the program maintain variety for the staff member.

Modification to the current schedule may need to occur.  Possibly, smaller numbers of people per session, with sessions being run more often, will solve the programming dilemma.  Above all, remember that clients are assigned to a participation category for scheduling purposes only.  The goal is for each client to participate at the highest level that he/she can attain.

## Summary

Clients have the following options with regard to a recreation experience.  They are:  avoidance, observation, or participation.  Avoidance may be due to fear such as the that the unknown, embarrassment, or of past experiences.  Observation is actually an early form of participation and clients should have the opportunity to observe.  Participation often begins with 1:1 activities in a person's room.  These activities must always be seen as non-threatening and enjoyable to the client.

The recreation experience has five phases, all of which may affect the client's willingness to participate in current or positive or negative.  Travel to the event may be pleasant or frightening.  The activity may be enjoyable or not meet up to the client's expectations.  Return travel may be the perfect opportunity to relax or be too long.  The last phase, recall, brings the other phases into focus in the client's mind.  The recall phase influences the value of the total experience for the person.

A quality recreation program provides opportunities for every client to participate at his/her own functioning level.  The amount and type of recreation participation for each client is determined by the level at which that person functions.  Participation may be categorized into five levels.  Those with *No Verbal Response* respond only to 1:1 sessions.  Those who are *Unable to Attend Group Programming* need to have 1:1 programming with the possibility of some small group activities.  The *Capable But Motivated Not To Attend* client requires the building of a trusting relationship with the recreation professional before he/she will attend activities outside of his/her room.  The next level, the *Selective* client, attends one or two activities regularly, but needs staff assistance to have a broader interest base.  The final category is the *Motivated* client who attends a variety of programs regularly.  People in this group need encouragement to initiate activities on their own.

A dilemma occurs when trying to schedule 1:1 sessions which are required to meet the programming needs of the lower functioning level clients while maintaining group activities for the higher level clients.  Modifications of the current program with better usage of early morning, lunch time and shift change hours for 1:1 sessions is one possible solution.

This chapter has focused on the motivation and participation levels of the clientele.  It is hoped that an understanding of why clients function as they do will aid the staff in their efforts to individualize the client's recreation program.  The following chapter presents information on program variety and balance.

# Resources

Chubb, M. and Chubb, H. (1985). *One Third of Our Time.* New York, NY: MacMillian Publishing Co.

*Dynamic Leisure Programming for Older Adults.* (1984). Alexandria, VA: NRPA Publications

Gault, J. (1983). *Free Time.* New York, NY: John Wiley and Sons.

Godbey, G. (1990). *Leisure in Your Life*, (3rd ed.). State College, PA: Venture Publishing, Inc.

Kimeldorf, M. (1989). *Pathways to Leisure.* Bloomington, IL: Meridian Education Corporation.

Mundy, J. and Odum, L. (1979). *Leisure Education.* New York, NY: John Wiley and Sons.

# PROGRAM DEVELOPMENT

# PROGRAM DEVELOPMENT

A quality nursing home recreation program provides opportunities for every client to participate at his/her own level of functioning.  A well-rounded program offers variety and balance in the programming efforts so there is something for everyone on a regular basis.  Therefore, determining the clients' needs and interests, as well as their functioning and participation levels, which were discussed in previous chapters, must be completed prior to establishing an overall schedule.

## Preparing Schedules

Schedules are a vital part of all recreation programs.  The recreation schedule, as in most other disciplines, falls into four categories:  yearly, monthly, weekly and daily.  The yearly schedule helps with the scheduling of seasonal special events, trips and holidays.  The monthly schedule provides added details and acts as a tool for staff planning, as well as stimulating client anticipation for coming events.  The weekly schedule details the activities in large time blocks while the daily schedule breaks the programming into actual increments of time.

Scheduling is more than changing dates on the corresponding previous schedules.  Every event and activity should be evaluated to determine if it continues to be appropriate for the clientele.  New ideas and approaches should be included in the program to keep it fresh and fulfilling for the clients and staff.

It is necessary to set blocks of time for regularly scheduled programs, but allow for flexibility in order to include special program offerings.  The clients anticipate that certain days of the week indicate certain activities, since older adults usually prefer a routine.  Over time the program may become so stagnant and boring that it loses appeal for the staff and sometimes the clientele.  If the program is stale, the staff members lose their enthusiasm and then the clients lose interest.  The solution is to keep the monthly and weekly programs from getting so heavily scheduled that they can not be easily adjusted.

A good way to keep flexibility is to offer categories of activities in time blocks on the schedule and then vary the activities within the time block on a weekly basis.  For example, Monday afternoon is set aside for "active games" such as volley ball, bocci ball, bowling, hockey, horseshoes, etc.  Then the program can be held indoors in winter and outdoors, during warmer weather.  The clients begin to think of Monday afternoon in terms of something physical, but the activity is varied so they don't become complacent and bored.  The same can be done with cooking activities, crafts and any number of programming ideas.  The discussion group could actually do charades or a version of "Win, Lose or Draw," or write a short story, instead of always discussing a reminiscent topic.  With this method of scheduling the staff can be more creative in their activity selection and therefore approach the experience with more enthusiasm.

## Varying The Setting

There is often a tendency to have all of the clients come to an activity area for the bulk of programming since the room was designed for the client's usage.  Although it is good for the clients to get away from their rooms, this overuse of one area limits the program offerings.  Transportation time must be added onto every program, which cuts down on the time for the activity. Also, clients who will not leave the floor or their rooms are not included in these group activities. Utilizing all of the possible settings for recreation helps to keep the program balanced. The parking lot can serve as a site for a carnival, the front lawn can become a nature trail, the dining room could become a dance floor and the client's room a small group meeting place. The use of a variety of settings for recreation programming will help the program remain dynamic and interesting for the clientele. Chapter 8 discusses programming resources.

## Utilizing Resources

Several years ago the authors met a recreation professional who was bemoaning the fact that she had no transportation to take her clients anywhere. Transportation should be approached in the same manner as utilizing facilities. Prove the need for transportation to the facility administrators by utilizing what is presently available on a continuing basis. Since the woman never took the clients anywhere she was unable to prove that she would do so once transportation was obtained. Utilizing local senior citizen transportation systems and/or the agency's present vehicles, whatever they might be, will prove that the transportation will be utilized and will add a new dimension to the program.

## Programming Areas

Along with utilizing all of the possible facilities to their fullest potential, a review of the areas of programming should be conducted. Categories of programming include arts and crafts, social/ discussion, drama/music, dance/exercise, sports/games and nature oriented activities. If the religious programming falls under the jurisdiction of the recreation department then religious activities may be an additional category. Areas of programming are not limited to those listed above however, the categories should be broad enough to include several program offerings under each heading. If there are activity offerings in all of the various categories, then the facility is one step closer to providing a balanced program. If most of the program offerings fall into one or two categories, then the program needs to be revised. Many traditional programs rely heavily on the arts and crafts area of programming and offer little to nothing in the performing arts such as music, dance and drama, or the natural environment. Further discussion follows utilizing these program areas.

The staff has to continually remember that client's interests are the most important factor in scheduling. Therefore, all types of programs must be offered and not just those which are easy for the staff to conduct. A search for a part-time employee or a good volunteer could fill the programming gaps. One of the present staff members might take a course or read additional materials in preparation for conducting new programs. Developing a new program can also be extremely motivating for the enthusiastic staff member.

# Program Formats

After determining all of the possible facilities (Chapter 8) as well as reviewing the schedule for a variety of programming areas, the schedule should be divided into program formats. The formats, in combination with facility review and programming areas, ensures a program which has breadth as well as depth. The concept of providing programming to every client at his/her functioning level becomes a reality, instead of just an idea.

Each individual learns and responds to situations differently. The program format method was developed to assist with schedule development. Currently programs are categorized into one of five formats, according to Farrell and Lundegren (1991). Recreation professionals working with older adults might determine that there is a need for additional formats, or for renaming those presented. The current formats, like everything else in this book, are meant to be idea generators and may be modified to fit the situation.

The concept behind the formats is that if there are program offerings in each category then there is an opportunity for all types of people to become involved in the program. There are no set standards in terms of the number of programs which would fall into each category. The assumption can be made that if the schedule is very heavy in one format, yet there are few programs offered under the other formats, the program is unbalanced. There is a worksheet following this section so the recreation schedule can be broken into the categories and reviewed. The five program formats are: *Educational/Classes*, *Club*, *Open*, *Special Event*, and *Competitive*. Each will be discussed in detail.

## Educational/Classes

The most common format, *education classes*, should be thought of as programs which have a leader who directs the group in the activity. The group follows the instructor's lead and the group would not function without the leader. The intent of classes with older adults may not be educational in the traditional sense, but the group meetings are opportunities to participate and practice a skill. In many cases it may be the opportunity to learn a new skill. For example, a craft class where people meet to do a specialized project or the exercise group with the instructor leading the group in their movements would fall into this format. With a little thought, the recreation professional should be able to understand that many of the programs fall into the education classification. There is a leader who directs the group's activity toward a goal. In some ways it is easier to look at the education format in terms of the process of elimination, if the program does not fit into the other formats it probably would fall into this category.

The education format is a comfortable one for the leader. Although the session takes planning, the leader controls the activity's direction. There is an opportunity for the person to participate on a continuing basis. Unlike educational classes in other recreation settings where a group might meet for six weeks or eight sessions, residential group experiences tend to meet on a regular basis forever.

To increase the benefit derived from educational programs, set a definite number of sessions for the program. This helps to keep the people motivated as they know the period of their commitment. For example, after six weeks the exercise group "graduates" and another group begins. They have successfully completed phase one and can now move into "Exercise Two" which may be perceived as more challenging. Many times clients don't want to join into a group they think is already formed. With this method new groups are forming all of the time so they can easily join in the next session. All types of activities, from discussions to craft classes, gardening or dance groups could be run in this manner.

Six to eight week sessions work best because there is enough time to observe some progress, yet not enough time for the client to become bored with the activity. Some programs may even be suited to one or two sessions such as the special craft of the month.

## Clubs

Whenever the members of a group get together on a regular basis and need minimal support from the recreation professional they might be considered as a *club*. The group is generally made up of individuals who already have similar skills or interests and need an opportunity to share their experiences. Clubs give people an opportunity to get together and socialize, they are a common part of society and should be fostered with older adults. Clubs provide clients with opportunities to be in leadership roles and make decisions. If the group requires intense leadership from the recreation professional it should not be considered as a club until the leader can turn more control over to the clients.

All clubs need to have some purpose. Many social clubs are designed to perform some good work, but it is fun to have some groups which are solely recreational such as the "card club." If the group is to be a club, the therapist and the clients must determine the purpose so the group can develop a sense of direction. Some agencies who have Women's or Men's clubs note that mostly women attend the Men's club and visa versa. In most of these cases, the clubs have no sense of direction and purpose. They are simply a time for the clients to get together for more free food. If it is a Men's club make it exclusive, even the leader should be a man, and determine the club's mission. Is it to provide recreation experiences for the men? Is it to help the men maintain or regain a sense of confidence? Keeping in mind the purpose for clubs as opportunities for people with a shared interest to get together to practice a skill will help determine the direction the club should take.

Clubs should meet regularly with the clients assuming as much of the leadership role as possible. The group should be encouraged to have special programs for members only or they may present programs for others. Such programs help the members to remain active and enthusiastic. One suggested club is the Soap Opera Group which meets in a client's room to discuss plots, guess what is going to happen next, and even write their own stories. They might even write the soap opera news report for the client newspaper. Another group could be the Sports Club which meets weekly to try to determine the winners in upcoming favorite sporting events. They might watch television sports together, and attend local games during the season. The fishing club might start at fishing license time, go fishing all season then end the year with a big fish fry for members. The garden club and card club are certainly familiar groups especially for women. The ideas for clubs are endless. It takes a little imagination on the recreation staff's part to get them started and coordination to keep them going. But the decision-making skills the clients practice are worth the efforts.

## Open

Clients should have an opportunity to participate in recreation activities on a drop-in or pick-up basis. Therefore, an *open* activity room or a games area should be a part of the recreation program. Drop-in types of activities where the clients visit for a short time to enjoy the experience, such as "coffee klash," happy hour or petting zoos should be scheduled regularly. The idea of a drop-in activity is to permit the client to participate at his own pace. Many people prefer to attend recreation experiences when and if they feel like it. They often prefer this spontaneous experience over those which are scheduled and conducted by a leader.

Open programs or facilities are such that the client can easily join or leave without missing any of the program. Open activities give the person an opportunity to practice skills in a spontaneous manner without making a commitment to the experience. Remembering that many of the clients need opportunities to observe before actively participating, open programming can provide that opportunity.

## Competitive

Most facilities do offer some competitive programming for the clients. *Competitive* events give the client the opportunity to test skills he/she possesses, against an opponent. The sense of accomplishment from participating in competitive events can increase the client's self esteem. Older adults need a challenge in their lives and competitive events can be that challenge. Modified team sports such as volleyball, hockey, and whiffleball develop team spirit and a competitive atmosphere. Individualized sports such as horseshoes, bocci ball, and croquet should also be encouraged. Even sporting events such as a modified basketball toss, the wheelchair obstacle course and Velcro™ darts can foster the competitive spirit which many of the clients need.

It is important to remember that not everyone will thrive on physically challenging experiences and opportunities. Competitive activities using the mind should also be encouraged. Checkers, dominoes, and spelling bees are just a few possible nonphysical competitive activities. Even larger groups can join in the competitive spirit with such events as a smile contest. Everyone's photograph is taken and displayed in a prominent area. Visitors, staff and clients cast votes for the silliest, cutest smile, biggest grin, etc.

Scheduled competitive events should include activities which are familiar, such as horseshoes, and those which are new such as a type of ring toss. Team activities as well as individual events which can take place in a short time period as well as those which continue for several days are also important considerations. A spelling bee can take an afternoon while the Olympic events take place daily for a week and a bowling tournament between units is conducted over a two month period. Competitive events should be an integral part of the ongoing program.

## Special Events/Performances

Recreation programs for older adults are among the best for providing excellent special events for the clients. Most facilities offer a minimum of one special program per month and most offer something slightly out of the ordinary at least once a week. Special events, including outings, add excitement to a schedule. They break up the routine and give everyone something to look forward to. Client involvement in planning increases anticipation of the special event and should always be encouraged.

In many cases, special events are an opportunity to indulge in often forbidden foods. Special programs and outings can be successful even if refreshments are kept at a minimum. Light snacks such as fresh fruit, or cheese and crackers, are healthy alternatives to the donuts, cake and ice cream that are often served.

Refreshments prepared by the clients are usually appreciated more and add an additional aspect to the program. Even if their contribution is to place cheese slices on plates and put crackers into bowls, this promotes client independence and involvement. Some agencies have food committees or clubs which help to provide the refreshments for events.

Currently most special events which are offered tend to be entertainment oriented. The client is a spectator watching someone else perform. Holiday parties, nursery school programs or music events are just a few of the activities where the clients are usually the observers. These types of events are necessary especially for that client who is afraid to be actively involved as a participant, yet there is a need for clients to be the performers.

Clubs or educational groups could occasionally be the entertainment at the special event. This would provide the sense of purpose and direction for the group as well as provide entertainment for the party. For example, the exercise group could demonstrate their routines during an open house, or the drama club could put on a production for a holiday party. Even the Men's and Women's groups could get involved by being models in a fashion show.

Whatever the occasion, clients should be encouraged to be involved in all of the phases of special event programming. Their involvement is the key to successful special event programming.

## Putting It All Together

After the program offerings have been divided into the five formats, the recreation professional should determine those areas where there are not enough activity selections, or where there are too many activities. There may be a need for additional formats based upon the specific needs of the facility.

To ensure that there are a variety of activities within the various formats, complete a form which looks at categories of programming in combination with each of the formats. For example, the category of arts and crafts. Does the facility offer opportunities within the arts and crafts category for competition, clubs, special events, open experiences and classes? An art show with the clients, visitors and staff judging the entries would be a competitive event. The quilting group could be the club and the special event might be a visit to an arts festival. A hobby shop or open craft period where everyone works on the project of his choice is an open experience and a class in candle making or ceramics would be the educational component. The Program Formats and Areas Analysis Sheet which follows [Figure 6] is designed for the recreation staff to categorize the various program offerings into the appropriate area.

It is not necessary to have events under each program area as well as format. There may be more than one event in each category in some instances. For example, under the sports category, the agency might offer volleyball, horseshoes, bocci ball and bowling all of which would be considered as competitive events. The idea is to determine whether or not there are large gaps in the programming efforts. For example, if there are no performing arts programs or a limited number of open events, then the schedule needs to be modified to include more variety.

| Program Formats and Areas Analyzation Sheet | | | | | |
|---|---|---|---|---|---|
| Program Areas | Program Formats | | | | |
|  | Education | Club | Competition | Special Event | Open |
| arts and crafts |  |  |  |  |  |
| music and drama |  |  |  |  |  |
| verbalization activities |  |  |  |  |  |
| dance and exercise |  |  |  |  |  |
| outdoor activities |  |  |  |  |  |
| sports and games |  |  |  |  |  |
| social recreation |  |  |  |  |  |

**Figure 6**   Program Formats and Areas Analyzation Sheet

The program format system is a tool to review the recreation program schedule for variety. It is not meant to be additional paperwork for an overworked staff. Rather it is meant to provide a check and balance system. The format system can act as a starting point for brainstorming. For example, if the staff discovers there is a need for additional opportunities for client performers or leaders, then the brainstorming will be focused toward that endeavor.

## Summary

Schedules should be dynamic and take advantage of a variety of settings and activity blocks. Flexibility is a key to keeping the staff enthusiastic and the clients interested. Reviewing the recreation schedule for adequate program scope is an important step in keeping the schedule dynamic. Program scope should include, but is not limited to, the following categories: social/discussion, arts/crafts, drama/music, dance/exercise, sports/games, and outdoor-oriented. In a balanced program, each of the program areas includes activities under the five formats. The formats include: education/classes, club, open, competitive and special event. The categories and formats can be expanded to include other specialty offerings such as 1:1 and religious activities.

The recreation staff are encouraged to list the program offering under each category and format utilizing the analysis sheet provided [Figure 6]. Large gaps in either areas or formats indicate imbalance within the program. The following chapter explores staffing a balanced program.

# Resources

Edgenton, C. R., Compton, D. M. and Hanson, C. J. (1980). *Recreation and Leisure Program-ming*: *A Guide for the Professional*. Philadelphia, PA: Saunders College Publishing.

Farrell, P. and Lundegren, H. (1991). *The Process of Recreation Program*, (3rd ed.) State College, PA: Venture Publishing, Inc.

Russell, R. V. (1982). *Planning Programs in Recreation*. St. Louis, MO: C. V. Mosby Co.

# NOTES

# STAFFING THE PROGRAM

# STAFFING THE PROGRAM

The recreation department of many residential facilities is often understaffed, underbudgeted, with inadequate facilities and equipment.  However, the majority of positive publicity for the agency is due to recreation activities.  Too often, the recreation staff is thought of as "the fun and games people," and recreation is something that anyone can do without professional preparation.

Improving the image of the recreation department is an ongoing task which will result in improved service to the clients.  Just as professional dress and grooming changes the image of a person, use of proper terminology improves the professional image.  The department image can be improved through the development of an operations manual, in-service programming and invitations to other departments to attend special events and outings.

In this chapter suggestions for an operations manual are made, a method for determining staffing requirements is presented and volunteers are discussed.  Staff motivation is also explored.

## Operations Manual

Creating a comprehensive department operations manual is one of the initial steps toward the development of a quality program.  Its aim is to define the purpose, function, responsibilities, and procedures of the Recreation Department.  It will also indicate to the other departments and to the administration that Therapeutic Recreation is a viable field and will document how this group of professionals serve as an integral part of the total team of care-givers.

The following outline is a sample of the items which should appear in a Recreation Department Operations Manual.

- Nursing Home Mission and Goal Statement
- Purpose and Function of Department
- Departmental  Responsibilities
- Inter and Intra-Department Relations
- Professional Staff Job Descriptions
- Volunteer Staff Job Descriptions
- Dress and Conduct Information
- Staff Scheduling
    - Weekday Schedules
    - Evening and Weekend Schedules
- Documentation Procedures and Examples
- Record Keeping Procedures
- Program Scheduling Procedures
- Daily Schedule Format
- Weekly Schedule Format
- Monthly Schedule Format
- Description of Major Events
- Special Event Planning/Scheduling Procedures

- Trips, Tours and Outings
    Examples and Scheduling Procedures
    Preparation of Clients
- Miscellaneous Tasks and Responsibilities
- Staff and Client Expenditures Procedures
- Budgeting Process and Examples
- Examples of Forms Used by Department

A comprehensive operations manual simplifies administration of the department, beginning with staff selection and training. It continues by simplifying the process of programming, documentation, evaluation and budget preparation. It is one of the keys to quality programming.

## Staffing Needs

How much staff is needed to run a quality program? To answer this question it must be determined how many hours of each type of programming is necessary. It begins with the client's needs assessment and the development of the goal plans. Reviewing the activity analysis will indicate the type of activities that are necessary. The final step is to develop a schedule that will allow each client to have the number of hours of programming that is necessary to meet the quality program goal.

Some programs are mainly staff oriented. This type of program is easily recognized, for as much as 90 percent of the programming is for 10 percent, or fewer, of the clients. Another indicator is the lack of weekend and/or evening programming. In addition, the programs are limited in scope and format, with little client input. Often the staff members in such a recreation department will spend less than six hours per day in direct client contact. ("Client contact" meaning working with clients in groups or on a 1:1 basis or transporting clients to and from events).

To qualify as quality program, all of the clients must be included, from the very lowest to the high-level functioning participants. There would be evening programming several times per week and weekend programming would include activities or events other than religious services.

To calculate the staffing necessary to achieve this goal, determine the hours necessary each week for those requiring 1:1 programming. Then determine the number of hours needed for small groups. Add in the hours for the various other types of programming and for the other staff duties that appear in the operations manual. The sum will be the number of staff hours necessary to meet the needs of the clients.

The following form [Figure 7] will help in calculating the number of staff necessary to provide a quality client-oriented program. Divide the total staff hours necessary by the number of hours each staff member is paid to work per week and the result will be the number of fulltime staff equivalents necessary for a quality client-oriented program.

The staffing needs may seem impossible to meet. It is often difficult to move from "what is" to "what should be." Reviewing the goals and staffing needs with the administrator is suggested as the first step in the solution of staffing needs. One possible solution is increasing the usage of volunteers. Qualified volunteers can help implement a client-oriented recreation program.

## Staff Time Requirements

1. *Optimum number of 1 : 1's for each week.*

| # wk. | | mins./each | min./hour | hrs./week |
|---|---|---|---|---|
| ___ | X | ___ | ÷    60 | = _____ |

2. *Number of very small groups (3-4 persons) each week.*

| # grps./wk. | | mins./each | min./hour | hrs./week |
|---|---|---|---|---|
| ___ | X | ___ | ÷    60 | = _____ |

3. *Number of small groups (5-8 persons) each week.*

| # grps./wk. | | mins./each | min./hour | hrs./week |
|---|---|---|---|---|
| ___ | X | ___ | ÷    60 | = _____ |

4. *Number of large group daytime activities each week.*

| # grps./wk. | | mins./each | min./hour | hrs./week |
|---|---|---|---|---|
| ___ | X | ___ | ÷    60 | = _____ |

5. *Number of evening and weekend activities each week.*

| # mo. | | hrs./event | | # staff/event | | wks./mo. | hrs./week |
|---|---|---|---|---|---|---|---|
| ___ | X | ___ | X | ___ | ÷ | 4 | = _____ |

6. *Number of special events scheduled each month.*

| # mo. | | hrs./event | | # staff/event | | wks./mo. | hrs./week |
|---|---|---|---|---|---|---|---|
| ___ | X | ___ | X | ___ | ÷ | 4 | = _____ |

7. *Number of trips and outings scheduled each month.*

| # mo. | | hrs./event | | # staff/event | | wks./mo. | hrs./week |
|---|---|---|---|---|---|---|---|
| ___ | X | ___ | X | ___ | ÷ | 4 | = _____ |

8. *Amount of time for program planning/preparation.*

| hrs./wk./staff member | | number of staff | hrs./week |
|---|---|---|---|
| _____ | X | _____ | = _____ |

9. *Amount of time for charting/goal writing.*

| hrs./wk./staff member | | number of staff | hrs./week |
|---|---|---|---|
| _____ | X | _____ | = _____ |

10. *Amount of time for staff meeting.*

| hrs./wk./staff member | | number of staff | hrs./week |
|---|---|---|---|
| _____ | X | _____ | = _____ |

11. *Amount of time for miscellaneous responsibilities.*

| hrs./wk./staff member | | number of staff | hrs./week |
|---|---|---|---|
| _____ | X | _____ | = _____ |

12. *Amount of time for inservice programs.*

| hrs./mo./person | | # persons | | wks./mo | hrs./week |
|---|---|---|---|---|---|
| _____ | X | _____ | ÷ | 4 | = _____ |

*Total Staff Hours for Therapeutic Recreation Program*    _____

total staff hours ÷ total hours each staff member is paid per week = number of fulltime staff _____

**Figure 7**  Staff Time Requirements

# Volunteers

An effective volunteer is a person who has available time and wishes to donate his or her services to a specific cause or program. It takes the same depth of commitment to be an effective volunteer as it does to be an effective employee. The only difference is the amount of service given each week and the fact that the volunteer staff member receives no financial remuneration.

A volunteer, just as an employee, works most effectively when there is a specific job description covering the work to be done. Volunteers want to work with the professional staff, not replace them. They should serve as an integral part of the Therapeutic Recreation Department. Volunteers should have challenging assignments commensurate with their present skills and have an opportunity to learn new skills to increase their effectiveness. Volunteers should not be used to replace paid staff but to enhance and enrich the program offerings. A properly recruited and trained volunteer contingent can significantly increase the quality of a recreation program.

There are three steps for preparing staff members, whether paid or volunteer, to accept the responsibilities and challenges of therapeutic recreation leadership. They are: orientation, pre-service and in-service training. Much of the initial orientation process should be covered in the operations manual. In the case of volunteers, there should be a separate volunteer manual. If there is no director of volunteers, the director of therapeutic recreation should prepare such a document for the recreation department volunteers.

Orientation simply informs the new person of the job details and the policies of the agency. It should include where to park, how to check in, what dress codes should be observed, where to leave coats, what procedures to use in case of illness, and similar details. Facility policies should include information on meals, room visitations, resident information, confidentiality, transferring residents, and any additional considerations that will affect the volunteer's service. A tour of the facility should be given and the orientation group should be welcomed by the administrator.

A well-planned pre-service program is well worth the staff time necessary for preparation and presentation. It is extremely important that all persons involved in the instructing of volunteers be well prepared. The new volunteer must feel that the pre-service presentations are valuable. To be challenging, the sessions must have the material presented interestingly, move along at a good pace and have a balance between activities and discussion.

Assigned readings, role playing and staff observation are valuable techniques to teach the skills. There should be time to practice a skill after it is presented along with demonstrations of leadership techniques. Opportunities for the trainee to lead activities with periodic evaluations of the progress should also be provided.

As the volunteers begin to use their new skills with the residents, additional challenges will arise. In-service or continuing education is important to the paid as well as the volunteer staff. New ideas and techniques may be presented by employees or volunteers. Volunteers should be encouraged to participate in workshops, conferences and adult education courses outside the agency. Such programs can result in a variety of new resources and ideas which may be shared with the entire recreation staff.

A corps of highly trained volunteers makes it possible to do a more programs. Trips, tours and outings are much more fulfilling for the residents when there is adequate staff to transport and meet their needs. The safety and comfort of the residents is enhanced by the use of volunteers.

Much of the planning and preparation for special events can be handled by volunteers under the direction of a professional staff member. The proper training and supervision of volunteers doesn't take time, but rather it makes time for innovative programming.

## Staff Motivation

One of the keys to quality program is a motivated staff. Staff motivation is dependent upon three factors: inspired leadership, adequate resources and an innovative program scheduling.

In many residential facilities, recreation is often very low on the list of priorities from administration's point of view. In spite of having the least facilities, the lowest budget, and the highest client-to-staff ratio, it is often the highest motivated group of staff members in the agency. However it is easy to feel trapped by the lack of staff and/or resources.

Inspired leadership can make a positive change. Assessing the problems, prioritizing them and developing a plan for change is the first step. Changing a program from staff-oriented to client-oriented may be more difficult if staff members do not see the need for the change. A revised operations manual which has received the endorsement of the administration is a tool that will be valuable in initiating change.

In-service programs are great staff motivators. Three types of in-service programs may be utilized. First, staff may attend an educational workshop one or more days in length. Getting away from the facility and talking with others in the same type of work will help improve morale and spark new enthusiasm. The second type of in-service is where the whole staff is not sent to the same workshop, only one or two staff cover the relevant presentations and then prepare a staff in-service to present the information to their fellow staff members. The third type is to have a consultant come to the facility and present an in-service, hopefully with a demonstration program involving clients.

It is important that each staff member feels that he/she is a vital member in the total team of care-givers. Periodic reports to the other departments and a willingness to do in-service programs for them will help in the process of educating the entire staff that recreation is more than diversionary activities. Involving the recreation staff in departmental decisions is important to staff motivation.

Upgrading a therapeutic recreation program is a continuous process involving all staff members. The staff should have input into every step of the model described in the first chapter. An involved staff is a motivated staff.

## Summary

Improving the image of the recreation department through client-oriented programming is a realistic goal. Analysis of program requirements and staffing needs is an important phase of this task. The selection, training and use of qualified volunteers assists in the implementation of an innovative program. Volunteers need guidance and a challenge, but are worth the staff time involved.

A motivated staff is another key to quality programming.  Attendance at workshops and in-services encourages enthusiasm.  The development of an operations manual provides valuable information for the recreation and other disciplines.  An operations manual helps all of the staff to see that recreation personnel are a vital part of the team of care-givers.

## Resources

Kraus, R. G. and Curtis, J. E. (1990).  *Creative Management in Recreation, Parks and Leisure Services*, (5th ed.)  St. Louis, MO:  Times Mirror/Mosby College Publishing.

# NOTES

# CHAPTER 7

# MEASURING PROGRESS

Why Evaluate?

Quality Assurance

Program/Event Evaluation

Effective Use Of Staff Time

Daily And Weekly Attendance Records

Monthly Reports

Summary

Resources

# MEASURING PROGRESS

There are four aspects of any operation that will benefit from an evaluative process. Administration, Personnel, Program and Facilities. Nursing home administration and facilities have a bearing on the recreation program, but evaluation of these areas is generally outside the jurisdiction of the recreation department. This chapter will focus on the two remaining areas of evaluation: Personnel (Leadership) and Program.

## Why Evaluate?

Well conceived on-going evaluation is an integral part of every successful therapeutic recreation program. In fact it is the key to a successful program. Following are some of the values that accrue from an on-going evaluation process.

- Monitoring of program impact and effectiveness by determining the extent to which goals are met.
- Gaining administrative support by weighing program benefits against costs.
- Developing rationale for additional programs, staff and budget.
- Exhibiting program legitimacy through documented progress and accomplishments.
- Aiding in program revision by determining whether an activity should be kept, revised or dropped.
- Improving staff morale through involvement in the decision-making process.

In addition to the above values, Quality Assurance Procedures require the monitoring, evaluation and documentation of the recreation program and leadership.

## Quality Assurance

The purpose of the quality assurance procedure is to pursue excellence through evaluation and monitoring programs to ensure that the needs of the clients are being met. The following steps outline the basic quality assurance requirements. Recreation departments following these procedures should have little difficulty in meeting the requirements of any quality assurance program developed by the facility administration.

- *Review the standards* of the recreation program, remembering that standards are minimal requirements.
- *Prepare a staff manual* which includes department procedures, job descriptions, program requirements, scheduling procedures, evaluation methods, record keeping standards and samples of forms used.
- *Assess client's needs and interests* utilizing this information in the development of care plans.
- *Update care plans* on a regular schedule.
- *Keep attendance records* for all activities.

- *Include activities required by Quality Assurance* on the program schedule.
- *Secure client input* on activities to be scheduled.
- *Evaluate programs and activities* on a regular basis.
- *Evaluate staff* on a regular basis.
- *Adjust programs* based on evaluation results.
- *Assess the effectiveness* of the adjustments and document improvements.
- *Communicate relevant information* to other departments through a regularly scheduled reporting procedure.

The following sections will explore procedures for program/event evaluation, effective use of staff time, leadership, keeping attendance records and documentation of the evaluative process.

## Program/Event Evaluation

It is essential that each program/event be evaluated as a part of the quality assurance procedure. An occasional written evaluation for each of the ongoing programs will document the extent to which the quality is being maintained.

Special programs/events should always have a written evaluation since it may be some time before they are repeated. The staff may forget improvements to be incorporated in the future if they have not been recorded.

A sample form is shown [Figure 8] which simplifies the evaluation task and keeps the information in a readily usable form. Such a form takes little time to complete, complies with quality assurance requirements and will simplify the task of planning a similar program/event at a future date. The evaluation form should be completed immediately following the event adding additional items as needed. A list of participants should be attached to the form and both should be filed with a copy of the planning and schedule that was utilized for the event. A loose leaf notebook is suggested as a method for keeping programs plans and evaluations easily accessible.

When the program/event is to be repeated, the evaluation will prove useful in revising and planning the event and scheduling the participants. If properly utilized, program/event evaluations make more staff time than they take, due to the added efficiency and program effectiveness that they promote.

**Program/Event Evaluation**

Event _____ Date_____ Time_____ a.m. /p.m.

Location_____ No. Participants _____ AMB ____ WC____

Program Objectives:


Schedule of Activities:


Leader Evaluation:  (Objectives, Size, Level, Flow, Length, etc.)



Reactions:  (Clients, Staff, Volunteers, Visitors)
    Positive:



    Negative:



Recommendations:  (Based on Above Information)
    Timing:


    Staffing:


    Volunteers:


    Group size:


    Level:


    Planning:


    Transportation:


    Other:

**Figure 8**  Program/Event Evaluation Form

## Effective Use Of Staff Time

Staff effectiveness is the main key to successful programming. The variety and type of programs, the number and quality of resident contacts, and the degree of social interaction among the clients are all dependent on staff effectiveness. The two components of staff effectiveness are individual abilities and, how staff members utilize their time. Periodic evaluation of these components will increase total program effectiveness.

Evaluation of staff abilities is best done through observation of the staff member in a leadership role. A form similar to the one which follows [Figure 9] may be used to evaluate both paid and volunteer staff. It is important that the observer be qualified and have a conference with the leader soon after the observation to go over the evaluation. Staff members can also benefit by observing each other utilizing the leadership evaluation form as a guide. It is recommended that peer leadership evaluation forms not be utilized as a basis for promotion. Results gained from use of staff leadership evaluation indicate the type of inservice programs which will be most beneficial to the paid and volunteer staff members. Role playing, video taping and demonstration of a variety of leadership techniques are possible inservice activities.

The second component of staff effectiveness, the use of time, must also be evaluated for successful programming. It is advisable for staff members to do a detailed analysis at least once a year. A minimum period of one week is suggested, with two weeks giving a more complete picture.

A Staff Time Analysis Form [Figure 10] can aid in determining how staff time is best used. It only takes a few minutes to record the time elements of an entire day. The sample time and activity recording sheet shows how a staff member can compile the information on a clipboard as the events occur. At first, the process may frustrate the staff, because it is often difficult to account for the day in 15 minute segments. However, when it is recorded as they go through their day, it becomes much easier. Utilizing the process helps to determine time use patterns. It also stimulates self evaluation which can promote the more effective use of staff time. One discovery which is often evident is that when clients are not available for group programming, there is time for several individual contacts.

Optimally, each staff member should be able to spend a minimum of five hours per day with direct resident contact. Direct contact means the staff member is with the clients during that time. Planning, preparation, record keeping, staff meetings and miscellaneous duties should take no more than two and one-half hours each day. A professionally trained, highly motivated staff should be able to spend as much as three-fourths of the day with the clients.

## Leadership Evaluation

Staff Member _____ Activity _____ Date __

Based on observation of the staff member leading an activity, rate the following items.

Observer _____

|  | 1<br>All the<br>time | 2<br>Most of<br>the time | 3<br>None of<br>the time | N/A |
|---|---|---|---|---|
| 1. All attendees can take part in the activity. | ___ | ___ | ___ | ___ |
| 2. Materials are suitable and well organized. | ___ | ___ | ___ | ___ |
| 3. Participants are greeted by name and know each other. | ___ | ___ | ___ | ___ |
| 4. Directions given clearly, briefly, and correctly without notes. | ___ | ___ | ___ | ___ |
| 5. Activity started on time and in an orderly manner. | ___ | ___ | ___ | ___ |
| 6. Helped clients complete an action without calling attention to their mistakes. | ___ | ___ | ___ | ___ |
| 7. Individuals and groups are praised and encouraged. | ___ | ___ | ___ | ___ |
| 8. Leader exhibited infectious enthusiasm at all times. | ___ | ___ | ___ | ___ |
| 9. No favoritism shown for any client or group. | ___ | ___ | ___ | ___ |
| 10. Prepared with alternate plans if activity was not successful. | ___ | ___ | ___ | ___ |
| 11. Activities met clients' needs and held their interest. | ___ | ___ | ___ | ___ |
| 12. Assisted clients who needed extra help. | ___ | ___ | ___ | ___ |
| 13. Incorporated clients' ideas in activity. | ___ | ___ | ___ | ___ |
| 14. Had a definite closing to the activity and thanked the clients. | ___ | ___ | ___ | ___ |
| 15. Evaluated the activity and noted changes for next time. | ___ | ___ | ___ | ___ |

**Figure 9**  Leadership Evaluation Form

**Staff Time Record**

Use 15 minute time increments

Date_____ Wing/Floor_____ Staff Member_____

| Time | Activity/Task | Comments/Participants |
|------|---------------|-----------------------|
|      |               |                       |
|      |               |                       |
|      |               |                       |
|      |               |                       |
|      |               |                       |
|      |               |                       |
|      |               |                       |
|      |               |                       |
|      |               |                       |
|      |               |                       |
|      |               |                       |
|      |               |                       |
|      |               |                       |
|      |               |                       |
|      |               |                       |
|      |               |                       |
|      |               |                       |

**Figure 10**  Staff Time Record Form

## Daily And Weekly Attendance Records

Under quality assurance procedures, client attendance must be documented. An Attendance Record used on a daily basis is an answer to this requirement. A form similar to [Figure 11] may be used on a clipboard by each therapist. The names of clients seen on a 1: 1 basis and those attending small group sessions can be entered directly on the form. Attendance lists for large group activities can be attached to the form. The large group activity should be noted on the form.

Although the time analysis form is used once or twice a year, the Attendance Record must be used on a daily basis by each therapist. Volunteers making interactive contacts with clients should also record them in a similar manner.

The weekly Client Contact and Staff Time Form [Figure 12, p. 62] is completed at the end of each day to record the number of contacts and time for each type of contact. It provides a simplified method for doing a weekly client contact and staff time analysis which is then utilized to compile the monthly report.

## Monthly Reports

An increasing number of Nursing Home Administrators require a monthly report from each department. Even if it is not a requirement, such a report from the Recreation Department will keep everyone informed of the contributions it makes to overall client care. It also provides the information necessary to support budgetary, staffing and facility requests.

The monthly report should include the following items:
- number of 1:1 contacts
- number of small group contacts
- number of programs by type and attendance
- number of special events by type and attendance
- list of outings and attendance
- list of staff meetings and inservices
- list of new programs with evaluations
- description of ongoing evaluations
- list of conferences and meetings attended
- news items that appear in the newspapers, on television or on the radio
- any relevant department news

A monthly report is a helpful tool in the evaluation and information dissemination process. Such a report should go to the administrator and to each of the department heads in the facility. It should be concise, easy to understand and have a logo or heading which shows that it is from the Recreation Department.

| Recreation Program Attendance Record | | | |
| --- | --- | --- | --- |
| Date_____ Wing/Floor_____ Staff_____ | | | |
| **Length of Time** | **Activity** | **Participants** | **Comments** |
|  |  |  |  |
|  |  |  |  |
|  |  |  |  |
|  |  |  |  |
|  |  |  |  |
|  |  |  |  |
|  |  |  |  |
|  |  |  |  |
|  |  |  |  |
|  |  |  |  |
|  |  |  |  |
|  |  |  |  |
|  |  |  |  |
|  |  |  |  |
|  |  |  |  |
|  |  |  |  |
|  |  |  |  |
|  |  |  |  |

**Figure 11**   Sample of Recreation Program Attendance Record Form

## Client Contact and Staff Time Summary

Week_____  Floor/Wing_____  Staff_____

| Activity/Task | Mon. | | Tue. | | Wed. | | Thu. | | Fri. | | Sat. | | Sun. | | Total | |
|---|---|---|---|---|---|---|---|---|---|---|---|---|---|---|---|---|
| | # | T | # | T | # | T | # | T | # | T | # | T | # | T | # | T |
| 1:1 with client | | | | | | | | | | | | | | | | |
| small group activity | | | | | | | | | | | | | | | | |
| large group activity | | | | | | | | | | | | | | | | |
| special event | | | | | | | | | | | | | | | | |
| outing/trip | | | | | | | | | | | | | | | | |
| | | | | | | | | | | | | | | | | |
| meetings/inservices | | | | | | | | | | | | | | | | |
| goal plans, program notes | | | | | | | | | | | | | | | | |
| | | | | | | | | | | | | | | | | |
| planning | | | | | | | | | | | | | | | | |
| miscellaneous tasks | | | | | | | | | | | | | | | | |
| | | | | | | | | | | | | | | | | |
| | | | | | | | | | | | | | | | | |
| totals | | | | | | | | | | | | | | | | |

Note:  # = List Number of Contacts
       T = Total Time in Hours

**Figure 12**   Client Contact and Staff Time Summary Form

## Summary

Administration, Personnel, Program and Facilities are the four areas of any agency which should be evaluated.  Nursing home recreation departments should concentrate evaluative efforts on program and personnel (leadership).

Program/event evaluations should be filed with the planning materials from each event for easy access by staff when the program is to be repeated.  A form for the evaluation is included. Staff effectiveness is a key to quality programming.  Suggestions are made for evaluating the two components, leadership ability and time management.  The use of the two evaluation formats, Leadership Ability and Staff Time Analysis, will improve both the effectiveness and the efficiency of the Therapeutic Recreation Program.

Quality assurance procedures require that a record be kept of client contacts and program attendance.  Program attendance and weekly record forms are provided to simplify this task. Weekly analysis and monthly reports are valuable tools in the evaluation process.  They provide a record of staff time use, programs completed, clients served, evaluative procedures utilized and changes that have been implemented.  Such documentation is a vital component of all quality assurance procedures.

## Resources

Farrell, P. and Lundegren, H.  (1991).  *The Process of Recreation Programming*.  (3rd. ed.) State College, PA:  Venture Publishing, Inc..

Kraus, R. and Allen, L.  (1987).  *Research and Evaluation in Recreation, Parks and Leisure Studies*.  Columbus, OH:  Publishing Horizons Inc.

Lundegren, H. and Farrell, P. (1985).  *Evaluation for Leisure Service Managers*.  Philadelphia, PA:  Saunders College Publishing.

Riley, B. editor (1987).  *Evaluation of Therapeutic Recreation Through Quality Assurance*. American Therapeutic Recreation Association.  State College, PA:  Venture Publishing, Inc.

# NOTES

# CHAPTER 8

# PROGRAM RESOURCES INVENTORY

**Program Elements**

**On-Site Program Resources**

**Community Resources**

**Program Master List**

**Program Implementation**

**Resources**

# PROGRAM RESOURCES INVENTORY

Insufficient budget, inadequate staffing and a lack of resident interest are the excuses most often used as reasons for a mediocre program. None of these excuses are valid! A positive attitude and approach will overcome most programming obstacles. A full range of on-site and community wide programming was provided at one 600 bed skilled and intermediate care county nursing home with a ratio of one recreation staff member to 120 clients. The methods utilized in the previous chapters were used to make this program a reality.

## Program Elements

The success of any program is dependent upon three elements: staff enthusiasm, innovative programming and client preparedness. To make any activity a quality experience for the clients it must include challenges, responsibilities and opportunities for decision making. To fulfill their therapeutic purpose, recreation activities must include one or more of these elements. The staff has the task of preparing the clients to meet the challenges, accept the responsibilities and become involved in the decision making process.

## On-Site Program Resources

The initial step involves a staff brainstorming session to develop a list of the full range of program resources that can be made available to fulfill the clients' needs and interests.

An inventory of the areas in and around the facility will reveal a number of potential program resources. Important requirements for any program site include easy access, safety and adaptability. Even though the site may not be completely suitable at present, look for possible adaptations that will make its use for programming possible. The following suggestions may help in conducting the inventory.

Indoor resources traditionally include the multi-purpose rooms, dining areas, television rooms, client rooms, and hallways as program sites. Perhaps other areas and program possibilities exist. The kitchen, laundry, maintenance shop and administrative offices offer possibilities for small group tours for the more alert clients. Explaining how meals are prepared and served, how the laundry is done, how maintenance is handled, as well as an introduction to the tasks that are performed in the offices, can be exciting tours for the clients. In a large facility, workers are usually happy to see the clients and to put faces with names they see every day as they prepare food or do laundry. Such tours tend to result in reduced complaints by the clients about the food and laundry.

After surveying the indoor areas for additional program ideas, continue the search on the grounds outside of the buildings. With an open mind, many additional opportunities can be found on the facility grounds or immediately adjacent to the facility. The following list of on-site program suggestions is based upon visits to agencies currently offering these programs.

## Outdoor Program Possibilities

Patio Area
- quiet activity
- active games
- raised gardens
- story telling
- exercises
- ice cream socials
- dancing
- nature crafts
- sing-a-longs
- walking area

Flat Grassy Area
- lawn bowling
- croquet
- raised gardens
- horse shoes
- quoit golf
- whiffle ball
- nature crafts
- garden plots

Parking Lots
- square dancing
- petting zoo
- bazaar
- carnival
- parade
- balloon volleyball

Sidewalks
- flower gardens
- art show
- walks for exercise
- craft fair

Wooded Area
- sensory trail
- picnics
- day camping
- nature activities
- cookouts
- adventure activities

Flat Roof Tops (where elevator service is available)
- greenhouse
- herbarium
- solarium
- flower pot gardening

# Community Resources

The community surrounding the facility offers a number of program resources. Experiences in the community are important for client well-being and are one sign of quality programming. Every effort should be made to solve the problem of transportation so that the clients can become involved in community activities. The following list suggests some of the community resources that have been used for programs.

## List of Community Resources

Shopping Tours
- malls
- craft fairs
- flea markets
- farm markets
- church bazaars

Cookouts
- county parks
- city parks
- commercial sites
- state parks
- private picnic groves

Historic Areas
- farm museum
- battlefields
- pioneer craft festival
- railroad museum
- county historical sites
- antique tool/machine club

Nature-Related
- nature centers
- fall color tours
- pontoon boating
- wading
- formal gardens
- fishing
- swimming

Eating Out
- church suppers
- restaurants
- fast food restaurants
- ice cream parlors

Sporting Events
- bowling
- basketball games
- soccer games
- ice hockey games
- baseball games
- harness racing
- football games

Animals
- farm visits
- kennels
- fish hatcheries
- zoos
- petting zoos

Social Events
- county fairs
- theatre
- carnivals
- Christmas light tours
- church socials
- band concerts
- art festivals

## Program Master List

Programming is too often accomplished by revising the previous month's schedule. The result is soon a sterile repetition of over-used activities. This approach tends to squelch staff innovativeness and enthusiasm. Refer to Chapter 5 for a review of program development procedures.

To assist in the scheduling of a dynamic program, prepare a categorized master list of activities from which to choose, leaving room to add new activities under each category. The example of such a list follows. It is suggestive rather than inclusive and is designed to serve as a springboard by a creative staff for developing additional activity ideas.

### Program Master List

Animals
- staff pet show
- resident animals
- zoo trips
- _____

- petting zoo
- farm visits
- circus trips
- _____

Audio-Visual
- movies
- photographs
- recorded music
- tape cassettes
- _____

- slide shows
- video tape activities
- recorded sounds
- _____
- _____

Music and Drama
- sing-a-longs
- folklore
- puppetry
- band concerts

- storytelling
- historical re-enactment
- skits
- wheelchair dancing

Arts and Crafts
- art shows
- watercolors
- silhouettes
- silkscreening
- clay modeling
- print making
- pioneer toys and games
- _____

- sketching and drawing
- worst drawing contest
- stenciling
- pudding painting
- leaf drawing
- whittling
- basketry
- _____

Food and Cooking
- baking
- butter making
- home made ice cream
- bake sales
- cookouts
- _____

- cake decorating
- jelly making
- salad preparation
- favorite food discussion
- picnics
- taffy pull

Horticulture
- flower arranging
- individual gardens
- ordering plants, seeds
- drying flowers for crafts
- _____

- window sill plants
- community gardens
- raising bird seed
- natural craft materials
- _____

Nature
- bird/animal watching
- astronomy
- building bird houses

- plant lore
- nature trail
- _____

Sports/Games
- horse shoes
- miniature golf
- quoit golf
- croquet
- broom hockey
- paddle tennis
- _____

- whiffle ball
- walking
- lawn bowling/bocci
- volleyball
- kickball
- _____
- _____

Community
- bazaars
- flea markets
- farm tours
- historic areas
- parades
- _____

- fairs
- farm markets
- factory tours
- state/county/city parks
- color tours in fall
- _____

Aquatic
- swimming
- fishing
- lake/river cruise
- _____

- wading
- boating
- activity observation
- _____

Verbalization
- alphabet game
- current events
- game show activities
  - Price is Right
  - Family Feud
  - What's My Line?
  - Name That Tune

- spelling bee
- old tools
- reminiscence
- _____
- _____

Special Interest Groups (Clubs)
- walking/hiking
- drama/storytelling
- health/exercise
- gardening
- musical instruments
- men's/women's
- _____

- baseball/football
- science fiction
- baking
- sewing/quilting
- choral
- home town
- _____

Special Events
- parties
  - newcomer's welcome
  - birthday tea/dinner
  - holiday celebration
  - _____
  - _____

- tournaments
  - wheelchair obstacle course
  - outdoor games
  - indoor games
  - _____
  - _____

- carnivals
- flea markets/bazaars
- craft demonstrations
- square/folk dances
- _____

- talent shows
- fantasy cruises
- Hawaiian luaus
- casinos
- _____

## Program Implementation

Quality Recreation Programs don't "just happen." They are carefully conceived by an enthusiastic and highly motivated staff to meet the needs and interests of all of the clients. When this programming approach is not used, the result is a stereotyped "BBC" program (where Bingo, Bible Study and Crafts are the major activity offerings). There is a need for the clients to have more exercise than going to BBC activities and to meals. A rocking chair does not give adequate exercise to promote good health. Regular sustained physical, mental, and social activities are necessary to minimize body deterioration. The challenge is to motivate the clients to participate. The activities and ideas presented in the remainder of this book, have been used with older adults resulting in enthusiastic client participation.

The Director of Recreation has the responsibility for keeping the staff current and enthusiastic, the program varied and balanced, as well as leading the effort of motivating and challenging the clients.

## Resources

Kennedy, D. Smith, R. and Austin, P. (1991). *Special Recreation: Opportunities for Persons With Disabilities*, (2nd ed.) Dubuque, IA: William C. Brown Publisher.

# NOTES

# CHAPTER 9

# ACTIVITIES TO PROMOTE PARTICIPATION

**Minimum Preparation**

**Some Preparation Needed**

**Initiating Interaction**

**Something Competitive**

**The Goal Is Interaction**

**Resources**

# ACTIVITIES TO PROMOTE PARTICIPATION

Instead of just stimulating thought and verbal response, the ultimate goal of therapeutic recreation is to involve clients in a variety of stimulating activities.

Activities which can be used with individuals as they arrive (First Comer Activities) also prove useful with the whole group to establish social rapport (Ice Breakers). The tone for the session can be set by using First Comer Activities and Ice Breakers to stimulate interaction with the leader and with other participants. Activities should be selected which have challenges that participants are able to meet and they must be presented in an age-suitable manner.

## Minimum Preparation

The following activities require a minimum of preparation and can be used on an individual basis or with groups of 10 to 12 clients.

### Waist Size

Provide a four-foot length of heavy string for each participant (the length may vary, but must be long enough to reach around the waist of the largest participant). While the clients are sitting at tables, have each person arrange his/her string in a large circle with the two ends touching each other.

Instruct them to take one end of the string and pull it around reducing the size of their circle until it is the size of their waist. They are not to lift the string or use their hands to measure the circumference of the circle. When everyone is satisfied that the circle is his or her own waist size, it is time to check the accuracy of the work.

A staff member or volunteer can mark each string and measure the person's waist with it. If the clients are capable, they can help each other do the measuring.

It will be found that most of them will have made their circle much larger than their actual size. After discussing how much they mismeasured, have them use the string to make an exact measurement. Holding the string at the measured spot, have each person lay it on the table and make a circle of the exact waist size. Most of the participants will be surprised at the smallness of the circle.

### Inchworm

Did you ever have an inchworm "measure you for a sweater?" This activity may be used indoors, but is better when the group is outside and a real inch worm is seen. Observe the inchworm closely and try to imitate its action.

To imitate the action of the inchworm, extend the thumb and index finger of one hand holding the other fingers against the palm Place the extended fingers against the other arm at the elbow. Bring the thumb to the index finger and then extend the index finger along the arm. Repeat the action until the "inchworm" can go no further and then reverse the action. Switch hands and have the "inchworm" crawl on the other arm.

A more complicated version is to hold the hands in front of the chest with the two thumbs touching each other and the index fingers together. Point the index fingers upward and, holding the left thumb and index finger steady, move the right thumb up to touch the left index finger. With the right thumb held against the left index finger, extend the right index finger into the air.

Holding the right fingers steady, move the left thumb up to the left index finger (against the right thumb which is also there). With the left thumb against the right thumb, extend the left index finger to touch the right index finger. Now move the left thumb up to meet the left index finger (which is against the right index finger). Keeping the left thumb against the right index finger, extend the left index finger upward. Repeat the action described in the first paragraph with the right hand.

Continue the action with each hand until the "inchworm" is as high as the client can reach then wiggle the highest index finder (just as the inchworm does when at the end of a twig). Now reverse the action and bring the "inchworm" back down. This is an excellent exercise in mind-hand coordination.

**Find Your Nose**

Instruct the participants to hold their nose with their right hand and to reach across and hold their right ear with their left hand. On the count of three, they are to release their nose and ear, clap their hands, then grasp their nose with their left hand and take hold of their left ear with their right hand. This action is much easier to understand when demonstrated by the leader as it is being described to the participants.

When the procedure has been practiced slowly several times, speed up the action. The ultimate goal is to be able to repeat the action correctly three times in a row. Even the most alert clients will find themselves reaching for "two" noses or will end up with one hand on each ear. By the end of the activity everyone will be laughing because it becomes quite hilarious to watch and to try.

# Some Preparation Needed

These activities will motivate participation but some prior preparation of materials is necessary.

**What's Missing**

This activity works well with up to eight clients at a time. Place 6 to 10 familiar items on a table and have the participants look at them for about one minute. Cover the items with a sheet. The leader then removes one item without letting the participants see it. When the cover is again removed, the clients try to decide what item is missing. The item is replaced and whoever guessed correctly gets to remove an item when the cover is replaced.

A variation is to have everyone memorize the placement of the items and when everyone's eyes are closed exchange the positions of two items. The clients decide which two items were moved.

The activity can be used indoors with items found there and is and excellent activity to use outside with items from nature. Have the clients select the natural items to be used.

**Hide in Sight**

Place 10 to 12 familiar objects around the room in plain sight. Make a list on a sheet of news print and have them see how many of the items they can find. They are not to remove the items or reveal where they are located until the leader asks.

This is a good first-comer activity. After everyone has arrived, have each person name an object and tell where it is located.

A variation is to have a list of the objects for each client and have them check off the items as they find them. Be sure to use an over-size typewriter to make the list.

Another variation is to have the client describe the item without naming it. The others are to identify the item. Be sure to take time to discuss the items that have been found. What is or was its use? The discussion is a very important part to develop interaction.

**Shadowgraph**

This activity needs a room with subdued lighting and a sheet suspended so that a single light source ( a slide projector works well) can be projected on it from behind. Collect a series of familiar items such as scissors, a comb, hair brush, a large spoon, etc., to be held between the light and the sheet so that a shadow of the object will be shown on the sheet.

Give each of the clients a turn at holding something up in front of the light. The rest of the group is to guess what the item is by looking at its shadow.

Using items from nature such as cattails, grape leaves and large pine cones adds an outdoor dimension to the activity.

# Initiating Interaction

The next three activities are often called "Action Socialization Experiences." They are excellent tools for the purpose of initiating interaction among the participants.

**Birthday Line**

Higher functioning clients can do this version of the activity. Have the participants stand in a small group and tell them they may not talk until after they have completed the instructions. Explain that they are to form a line with the person whose birthday is closest to January 1 at one end and arrange themselves in chronological order by day and month with the person whose birthday is closest to the last day of December at the other end. They may make signs with their hands but can have no verbal communication until they are all in line. When they are all lined up, have them each tell their birthdays in order.

Intermediate level clients may be asked to give their birthdays and with the help of staff members line their chairs up in chronological order. They then give their birthday and discuss how many have winter, spring, summer, or fall birthdays.

Whichever variation of this activity is used, be sure to discuss favorite birthdays they remember and favorite presents they may have received.

**Birth Year**

This activity works well with fairly low-functioning clients.  Have each person state the year that he or she was born.  The participants are then assisted forming a line with the oldest person on one end and with everyone in order of the year of their birth.

Questions for this activity might be, "What is our earliest memory?" "Did you have older/younger brothers or sisters?" "What birthday was the most outstanding?"

The birthdate activity may not be appropriate for some clients who do not want to tell their age.  It seems that this is not a problem for most older adults who are extremely proud of their longevity.

**Height Line**

To use with mobile clients, have them line up in order of height with the tallest person at one end and the shortest person on the other.  This activity takes little time and gets the clients on their feet.  A discussion might follow about the advantages and disadvantages of being tall or short.  The discussion often results in a variety of interesting stories from the clients' past experiences.

The clients that cannot stand may still participate in a  variation of the height line.  They remember the height they were at their "prime."  Ask each person to state their height and have them line up according to that height.  The same type of discussion can evolve from this group.

## Something Competitive

Competitive activities often offer opportunities to promote participation.  To be effective the competition should be very "low key."

**Human Tic-Tac-Toe**

This comes under the quiet but active heading.  Lay out a large tic-tac-toe "board" (nine three-foot squares) with chalk on the patio or parking lot.  It can be played indoors using masking tape if the tape is removed immediately after the activity so it doesn't mark the floor.

Line up the players in two teams and give each team a different colored ribbon or scarf to wear for identification.  The first person from one team moves onto one of the squares followed by the first person from the other team moving to another square.  Play just like regular tic-tac-toe but do not permit team members to coach the player moving onto the "board."

**Rock, Scissors, Paper**

This is a quiet game that uses more arm than leg activity.  The players are lined up in two lines facing each other.  Prepare six pieces of poster board, 8" x 16" and print the word "rock" on two boards, "scissors" on two, and "paper" on two.  Show how to use the following signals— "rock" is shown by placing the fist of one hand on the other upturned palm; "scissors" is shown by holding the first and second fingers of one hand in an open scissors position; "paper" is shown by holding an outstretched hand palm down.

Explain that rock breaks scissors, scissors cut paper and paper covers rock.

Select an alert client from each group and have them sit in the middle facing their own teams. Give each of them a set of the three cards. Since they are sitting back to back they can not see what card the other one is showing his/her team. Ask them to choose a card to show their team. After the team has seen the card, the staff member counts "one, two, three" and both teams show their designated signal. The team with the dominant symbol wins the point. Change the persons giving the signals after four or five turns. Before the activity begins, the staff member should set the number of points needed to win.

**Tree Detectives**

The out-of-doors is the best place for this activity. To prepare, make a full-size sketch of a leaf on a 4" x 6" card. Prepare a card for each of the types of trees found locally. Print the name of the tree on the side with the drawing and on the back of the card print some interesting information about the tree. Tree identification books should be available at the local library to help volunteers prepare the cards. Protect both sides of each card with clear contact paper so they may be reused.

Gather leaves from nearby trees and have the clients match the card they have been given with a leaf. The information on their card is then shared with the others.

## The Goal Is Interaction

The activities presented in this chapter act as first-comer activities, program starters, or as a change of pace in the program. The leader should utilize additional programs with these to promote socialization. Suggestions for sensory awareness and conversation appear in the next two chapters.

## Resources

Buckeye Leadership Workshop. (1991). *Leadership Handbook*. 16721 Hartford Road, Sunbury, OH 43074.

Hindman, D. A. (1978). *Kick the Can and Over 800 Other Active Games and Sports*. Englewood Cliffs, NJ: Prentice-Hall, Inc.

Le Fevre, D. N. (1988). *New Games for the Whole Family*. New York, NY: Putnam Publishing Group.

# USING THE SENSES

## USING THE SENSES

A deterioration of the senses is a normal part of the aging process. However, the senses seem to dull more rapidly when they are not stimulated on a regular basis. On the other hand, many clients, especially those in a residential facility, have "tuned out" the senses, especially the sense of hearing and smell, due to over-stimulation. The activity analysis, proposed in Chapter 2, will reveal how many activities make use of the senses.

Sensory activities should stimulate the senses which are still functioning. The activities should be fun, challenging and client appropriate. The staff members have to approach sensory stimulation activities in an enthusiastic manner to encourage client participation and interaction.

The following activities have been used successfully on a 1:1 basis and with small groups of clients functioning on a very low level. With little variation, they have been used as small group activities to stimulate social interaction between higher functioning clients. Some of the activities are particularly useful with the more alert clients in an outdoor setting.

Sensory activities should be introduced into the program gradually. Limit both the variety of sensory experiences and the length of the activity, remembering that overstimulation of a sense can cause the client to "tune out." As with any recreation activity, the session should be terminated while client interest is still high. Sensory activities, properly used, can be a basis for a discussion, or as a bridge to another activity.

The following section suggests sensory stimulation activities for the senses of *touching*, *seeing*, *hearing*, and *smelling*. The sense of *taste* has not been discussed since it is usually utilized on a daily basis.

### Touch And Tell

The sense of touch involves textures, size, weight and shape. Activities should be adapted to the client's level using any or all of these elements. Most people rely on seeing an object to know how it "feels." As sight deteriorates, the sense of touch is often lost. The following activities help the client to identify objects using only the sense of touch.

### It's in the Bag

Provide a heavy paper bag for each client in the group. Each bag should contain different familiar objects. Each person is asked to reach into the bag and without looking, identify the object by feeling it. Interaction is encouraged by having each person remove his/her object in turn. Discussion should focus on some aspect of the object's use.

For example, the object might be a tennis ball. The leader might ask: "What kind of ball is this?" (tennis), "Where is it used?" "Who are the major players today?" are other questions the staff might ask the clients. Trying to bounce or hit the ball with an oversized racquet (purchased in the toy section of a department store) might be all that the lower level client can accomplish. However, the staff should continue working with various familiar objects asking questions when appropriate in an attempt to elicit a response.

A variation of the "object in a bag" activity, for the more alert groups, would be to place 10 or more items in one bag. The bag is passed around the circle, each person identifying a different item by the sense of touch. None of the items should have sharp edges. Familiar items from everyday life such as a comb, toothbrush, sock, whistle and spoon could be used. Natural items such as walnuts, hickory nuts, acorns and pine cones can be used as a variation for more alert clients.

## Under the Table

The clients sit around a table and pass a familiar object from one to another under the table (no peeking). Everyone must refrain from identifying it until it has gone all around. Discuss size, shape, weight and texture before anyone identifies the object. Apples, oranges, pine cones, stones, buttons and similar items can be used.

## Feely Socks

Insert a one-pound coffee can in an old athletic sock. The purpose of the can is to make a compartment inside the sock in which a familiar object can be placed. Prepare several feely socks and use table tennis balls, combs, acorns, pine cones and similar items as objects.

Pass one sock around the group. As each person reaches into the sock and feels the item he/she makes a comment about the size, shape, weight, or texture of the object without revealing its name. After everyone has done this, they may guess what it is before removing it from the sock.

High-functioning clients can each be given one of the feely socks. Each person describes the item by the way it feels and the rest of the group try to guess the identity.

## Country Store

This activity is suitable for lower level clients who might not be able to play the feely sock game.

Cut a 6" square "door" in one end of a box that is about two feet square. Decorate the box to look like the outside of an old country store. Place familiar items inside the box that might have been found in such a store. Items such as a Mason jar lid, jar rubber, nail, screw, corn cob pipe, and baby powder can be used.

Have the person reach in and get an item (or the staff may have to bring out the item for the very low level client) and discuss the item and its use.

## Texture Cards

Staple or cement 2" x 3" pieces of material with distinctive textures to 4" x 6" pieces of posterboard. Sheet plastic, nylon net, wool and cotton cloth, upholstery material, plastic foam, sand paper and similar materials may be used. Have the clients compare these textures with items around the facility having similar textures. Comparing with natural items such as leaves, flowers, bark, or stones works well, also.

To use with lower level clients who cannot manage the individual cards, secure several of the texture swatches to a 10" x 14" piece of hardboard. Even very low level clients whose hand must be guided to matching textures often show a smile or make an audible response when the matches are felt.

# Hear, Here

Hearing impairments fall into categories from loss of certain frequencies to selective hearing. Due to the many sounds that are constantly heard in a facility, clients tend to "tune out" much of the "noise." This selective hearing finally amounts to not hearing anything unless the client practices "listening." The following activities are designed to help rehabilitate the tuning-in process.

## Ring a Bell

Use a small cow bell or hand bell for this small group activity. Explain that when a person is given the bell he/she is to ring it. The other clients then call out the name of the person who rang the bell. A variation is to have the leader ring the bell over a client's head and have the others say the name. In another variation, a group of 10-12 higher functioning clients is seated in a circle. Place one person in the middle of the group. Have the group pass a small bell from person to person as secretly as possible. The bell is to be rung whenever the person in the middle isn't watching. If the ringer of the bell is named, he/she becomes "it."

## Shaky Cans

Cover one pound coffee cans with colored contact paper. Place a familiar item such as a spool, thimble, marble or a washer in each can and close it with the plastic lid. Pass the can around and have each person shake it and try to guess the contents. After each person has had a turn, have someone open the can and show the object.

A variation with higher level clients is to have each person shake the can and make a comment about the object or sound it makes, such as "It's heavy," "It's flat," "It's round," until everyone has had a turn. Then try to guess the identity of the object before opening the can.

When using shaky cans in the out-of-doors, use natural objects such as pine cones, stones, sticks, or acorns in the cans. Ask the clients to find objects to use after they have identified the ones selected by the leader.

## Familiar Sounds

Make a tape or secure recordings with familiar sounds. Residential facility sounds such as those found in the dining room, whirlpool bath, a shower running, typewriter, sewing machine, or car could be easily recorded. Sounds of trains, boats, trucks, merry-go-rounds, and airplanes are a little more difficult but often radio stations will have a sound effects recording and could make the tape. Libraries are a good source for environmental recordings. Bird song tapes are readily available at nature centers but need to be edited for the songs of birds that are most familiar.

After hearing a sound the leader can stimulate discussion as to where one might hear the sound, the images it evokes and the last time it was heard.

## Smell And Smile

The sense of smell seems to deteriorate rather quickly as some people become older. An odor has to be very strong before it can be detected. For this reason, it is important that the clients have an opportunity to utilize this sense in a positive manner. Besides calling a client's attention to the obvious smell of flowers, baking, and newly turned soil, the following activities should aid in exercising the olfactory senses.

### Fruit Tray

A tray of selected ripe fruits is placed where a small group of clients can see it. The leader selects an item to let each person see and smell. It is best to start with lemons or limes and progress to oranges and bananas which may be peeled and eaten.

To isolate the smell from the sight, place the item in a cloth or paper bag. Cutting into the skin of the piece of fruit will release more of the distinctive smell when it is held for the clients to smell. Vegetables such as onions and garlic may also be used, but only one strong scent per session.

### Smelly Cans

Use a paper punch to make several holes in the plastic lids of one pound coffee cans. Place a banana or orange in the can. In a small group, let everyone smell the odor that comes through the holes in the lid before they guess what it might be. After it is guessed, the fruit may be peeled and cut into sections for each person to have a taste.

### Spice of Life

Plastic 35mm film containers are easily obtained at photo shops. They are excellent containers for this activity. Prepare a list of commonly used spices and put a freshly ground sample in each container. Place a cotton ball on top of the spice to keep the contents from spilling and to prevent the clients from seeing them. Recap the containers and allow them to stand for several hours before use. Number the containers to correspond with a master list and store them in a cardboard box or other container for ease in transporting.

It is important to limit each client to the identification of three or four fragrances in a session. Remember, their sense of smell is not as developed as it was at one time. Once the spice has been identified, a discussion can be guided toward the foods in which it would be used.

The film cans will keep the fragrance fresh enough to use with this activity for about a week before new spices must be added.

## Woodland Smells

This activity takes some preparation. It is most easily used in an outdoor setting where the materials are readily available.

Collect twigs from bushes or trees that have a distinctive fragrance. Sassafras, wild black cherry, black birch, spice bush, white pine, balsam fir, and red or white cedar are examples. Have the clients smell the twigs and discuss their preferences, as well as past uses.

## Herb Garden

Common herbs may be grown in pots or in planters around the patio. Break off small pieces of fresh herb for the clients to smell or taste. Encourage a discussion of the use of herbs in cooking. Many of the clients will remember using herbs for medicinal purposes, too.

# Look And Like

Recognition of colors, shapes and sizes are skills which also deteriorate in the aging process. Much of the deterioration is due to lack of use of the skill. The following activities have proven useful for providing the clients with an opportunity to practice these skills.

## Color Cards

Prepare 3" x 5" pieces of bright colored construction paper (stay away from the subtle shades). Cover each piece with clear contact paper (both sides), for a longer card life. Use a rubber band to hold the "deck" together. In a small group, give each person a different color. Encourage each person to name the color and to point out something in the room that is the same color. Swatches of cloth, flowers, or other colorful items placed on a table will make the activity easier for the clients.

When using the activity with low level clients it may be desirable to attach several colors to a 10" x 12" piece of hardboard and use the activity on a 1:1 basis with a client.

In the out-of-doors matching card colors with fall leaves or flowers is a stimulating and enjoyable activity. It is important not to give them too many colors at a time. One or two cards given to a pair of clients will often stimulate interaction between them.

## Shape Cards

Draw free-hand shapes on 3" x 5" cards, one shape on each card. Suggested shapes are circles, triangles, squares, spirals, ovals, stars and diamonds. Free-hand drawing is suggested so that clients will not think they have to look for perfect shapes.

In a small group, give each resident a card and have them look for something in the room with a similar shape. Doors, windows, clocks, mirrors, picture frames and other familiar items will match the shapes on their cards.

Gather leaves, stones, twigs and other natural items and place them on a table. Have the clients find an item from nature to match their cards. This activity can be used on an outing to a park where they can actually look for a natural item to match a card given them. The activity can be used with lower level clients if several shapes are drawn on a larger piece of construction board. Cut shapes out of cardboard and have the client match the cut-out shape with the drawing.

## Stacking Cans

This activity is useful for confused clients in reinforcing the concept of "larger or smaller" and "same size." It is patterned after the stacking box game for children. Start with a #10 can and collect cans of varying size that will fit inside each other. Make two sets, one for the leader and the other for the client. They may be covered with colored paper or left with their original labels.

A good activity is to have the client remove the cans one-by-one and then put them all back in the largest can. Another is to turn the cans upside down and stack them.

The leader can choose a can from one set and have the client find one of the same size from the other set. Finding one larger or smaller may also be a challenge. Many more variations for this activity can be devised by an innovative leader.

## Picture Cubes

Four to six 3-inch plastic photo display cubes are needed to prepare for this activity. Any cubes of a similar size may be used, but the picture cubes seem to last longest.

Choose four pictures 6" x 6" or 6" x 9" (depending upon the number of cubes) that represent the four seasons. Cut the pictures in 3" x 3" squares and mount one of the squares on each of the cubes. When the cubes are stacked correctly a complete picture from one of the seasons will be seen. Each cube will still have two unused spaces. Fill these spaces with 3" x 3" pictures of activities that take place in the various seasons.

This activity is best used on a 1:1. For the lowest level clients make up cubes with colored paper and have them stack them so that all of the colors showing are the same.

Another variation is to use 3" x 3" pictures of local landmarks to stimulate memory and interaction.

## Integrating With Other Activities

Sensory stimulation activities can be used in 1:1 or small group sessions with lower functioning clients. They are also useful as first-comer and socialization initiators with higher level groups. They are especially successful for either purpose if introduced indoors and used outdoors on picnics or outings at a later date. Many additional variations can be developed by the innovative recreation leader.

## Resources

Cornell, J. B. (1979). *Sharing Nature with Children.* Nevada City, CA:  Ananda Publications.

Van Matre, S. (1972). *Acclimatization.* Martinsville, IN:  American Camping
    Association

van der Smissen, B. and Goering, O. H. (1965). *Nature Oriented Activities.* Ames, IA:  The
    Iowa State University Press.

# CHAPTER 11

# CONVERSATION AND INTERACTION

Simple Recall

Familiar Topics

Activities From The Past

Table Fun

Maximizing Social Interaction

Resources

# CONVERSATION AND INTERACTION

One of the most difficult tasks for many leaders is getting the clients to initiate conversation with other clients. Of course, there are a few who are constantly talking and some that will speak to the staff, however a great number will only respond when someone else initiates the interaction.

The following activities are useful for helping clients initiate conversation and interaction. They can be used in small groups or as conversation starters on a 1:1 basis. Some of them are good activities to use with clients on a trip and others may prove useful for entertaining the group while waiting for a special program to begin.

## Simple Recall

These activities are "quickies"; they take no preparation and can be used over and over by simply changing the category.

### The List Goes on

Ask the clients to name as many things as they can think of under each of the following categories.

- states
- towns
- flowers
- fruits and vegetables
- birds and animals
- people's names

A variation of the above activity is to start with the letter "A" and see how many items they can name beginning with that letter and then proceed through the alphabet. Another is to have the first thing named begin with "A," the next with "B" and continue through the alphabet.

### Old Proverbs

The leader says the first part of the proverb and the clients complete them. The clients will often have proverbs to add to the list.

A stitch in time_____(saves nine).
Too soon old_____(too late wise).
The early bird_____(gets the worm).
Early to bed, early to rise_____(makes a man healthy, wealthy, and wise).
An apple a day_____(keeps the doctor away).
A penny saved_____( is a penny earned).
A bird in the hand_____(is worth two in the bush).
You can never be too thin_____(or too rich).
The grass is always greener_____( on the other side).

**Weather Sayings**

Complete each of the sayings and let the clients decide if they are accurate.

When there's a ring around the moon_____(it means rain is coming soon).
Rain before seven_____(clear by eleven).
Red sky at night_____(sailors' delight).
Red sky in the morning_____(sailors' take warning).
Evening red, morning gray_____(sets the traveller on his way).
Evening gray, morning red_____(makes the rain fall on his head).
Woolly worms heading south_____(means a harsh winter).
If the ground hog sees his shadow on February 2nd_____(there will be 6 more
    weeks of winter).
When the wind is in the south_____(it blows the bait in the fishes' mouth).

# Familiar Topics

Questions can often stimulate clients to talk to each other as well as to the staff. Once the clients start talking, let them go and see where the conversation takes them. It isn't necessary for the leader to keep pulling them back to the original topic. The leader may have to insert a question when the conversation slows down, but with a little practice the clients will soon be able to sustain converstions for twenty minutes, or more. Make sure everyone has a chance to participate and one person doesn't dominate the conversation.

When first asked what they would like to talk about the clients will usually say, "Oh, you decide," but after a few sessions they will begin to have suggestions. Magazines like *Good Old Days* and *Ideals* often have articles that would appeal to the clients. *Modern Maturity* magazine is also an excellent source for conversation ideas. Conversation starter ideas are limited only by the imagination of the leader.

**Work, Home and School**

These topic ideas will be enough to get the program started.

- What kind of work did you do? What were the hours? How far did you have to
    travel? What did you carry for lunch?
- Did you ever live on a farm? What time did you get up? What chores did you
    have to do?
- Did you have a garden? What did you grow? How did you preserve the produce
    for winter?
- Have you ever driven a car? What kinds of cars did your family have? When did you
    get a drivers license?
- Where did you go to elementary school? How many children were in your class?
    What was your best subject? Which subject did you like the least?
- What was your favorite game as a youngster? How was it played? What other
    games did you play?

## Open End Statements

The use of open end statements is another method of stimulating responses from the clients. Start with statements that have simple responses and as the clients get used to the activity more complex statements may be used. The responses to selected statements make interesting items for inclusion in the resident newsletter.

The following statements are examples of the type which may be used for this activity.

- My favorite activity is _____.
- My favorite time of year is _____.
- My favorite food is _____.
- The place I would like most to visit is _____.
- If I had a million dollars I would _____.
- I like (insert a topic) because _____.

## Landscape

Use a large map of the community, with a copy for each person in the activity. An alternative is to make a large sketch map that everyone can see. Mark a route on the map with which the clients are familiar. Ask the clients to identify as many points of interest along the route as possible. In a town they might locate the firehall, churches, businesses, parks, and any other landmarks they can identify. Where possible, take them for a ride over the route to see how many of the items were correctly placed.

This activity is a good lead-up activity for a trip to a familiar site, but it can also be used as a method for stimulating recall after a trip has been taken.

## Objects From the Past

Interaction and conversation can be stimulated by the use of old hand tools and household items. Perhaps a staff member or volunteer collects such items and would be willing to share them for this activity. Often enough items may be borrowed from various sources in the community to utilize on a short term basis. Contact the local library for the loan of Bi-Fockal materials. If they don't have the materials they can usually secure them on interlibrary loan.

Several methods are suggested for using the items for an activity. For a small group activity, select several items and show one item at a time to the group. Have them tell how it was used and let them discuss memories brought about by seeing it again. For a larger group the items can be placed on tables set up in the room. Each item is identified by a numbered card. Each participant is given a list of the items in alphabetical order and they must view the items and place the numbers by the name of the proper item. Another method is to give each person a blank sheet of paper and let them see how many of the items they can name correctly. More interaction is stimulated by having the clients work in small groups, than individually. After the group has named as many as they can, have them reminisce about their favorite items.

Some questions which may be used with selected items include:

- Curling Iron: How was it heated?  How did you tell when it was hot enough?
- Lunch Pail:    What did you carry for lunch?  How was it wrapped to stay fresh?
- Horseshoe:    What is the proper way to hang it for luck?  How many times a year were horses shod?
- Other Items: Ask similar questions relating to uses.

# Activities From The Past

Many activities or tasks that were done by the clients in their younger years can be utilized in recreation programs to stimulate interaction and conversation.  Any time a small group participates in a familiar activity the leader can initiate the interactive process through a series of questions and comments to the participants.  Such questions as "How often did you do this?", "How was it done?", "What are your favorite memories about it?", will often be enough to help the clients begin to share their memories.

## Special Dinners

These dinners provide an opportunity for several people to plan, prepare and eat a meal of their choice.  After clean-up is complete they can stay and share their thoughts.  The participants may be members of a special interest group or a client who is depressed and needs special attention (have the person invite three friends to participate).  Over the period of several days, the group plans the menu, purchases the food (or orders it from the dietary department) and makes table decorations.  The evening of the meal they prepare the meal with the help of a staff member or volunteer.  After dinner and clean-up they should have time to continue the conversations before returning to their rooms.

## Butter Making

This small group activity will bring back many memories.  A pint of heavy cream (not whipping cream) and two plastic one pound peanut butter jars (or similar) with screw-top lids are needed.  Place two heavy rubber bands around each jar to make them easier for the clients to hold.  Pour half of the cream into each jar and screw the lid on tightly.  If the cream has been at room temperature over-night it will make better butter.  Have the clients take turns shaking the jars.  Make certain that they pass them on to the next person before they get tired.  Continue to shake the cans until the butter "balls up" in the buttermilk.  Save the buttermilk (someone will want to taste it) and place the butter in a plastic bowl and wash it in several changes of cold water until the water is clear.  Salt the butter lightly and have some crackers to spread it on so that everyone gets a taste.

## Other Activities

Many activities will stimulate socialization in the same manner as those described.  Old recipes will give the necessary ingredients.  Here are some ideas that have proven successful in several programs.

- bread and biscuit making
- no-bake cookies
- taffy pull
- homemade ice cream
- corn roast
- marshmallow toast
- breakfast cookout

## Table Fun

These activities may be done on an individual basis but by using a "team" approach they become interactive. They can be used at the table while waiting for meals, on picnics and outings, or almost any time when there are a few minutes available. Prepare the lists in advance and have a supply of pencils available.

### Nature Word Scramble

Rearrange the letters shown to spell the names of familiar birds and trees.

| Birds | Trees |
|---|---|
| 1. obbthiew _____ | 1. northpapel _____ |
| 2. diigrbnk _____ | 2. panes _____ |
| 3. eebhop _____ | 3. clouts _____ |
| 4. accefhlrty _____ | 4. ample _____ |
| 5. cdfhignlo _____ | 5. has _____ |
| 6. ahkwtihgn _____ | 6. cared _____ |
| 7. acegklr _____ | 7. mug _____ |
| 8. achnttuh _____ | 8. atpacal _____ |
| 9. arprswo _____ | 9. amcus _____ |
| 10. eiorv _____ | 10. redreylerb _____ |
| 11. abelrrw _____ | 11. reegvneer _____ |
| 12. ceedkooprw _____ | 12. usthcten _____ |

ANSWERS: Birds: 1. bobwhite; 2. kingbird; 3. phoebe; 4. flycatcher; 5. goldfinch; 6. nighthawk; 7. grackle; 8. nuthatch; 9. sparrow; 10. vireo; 11. warbler; 12. woodpecker.

Trees: 1. thornapple; 2. aspen; 3. locust; 4. maple; 5. ash; 6. cedar; 7. gum; 8. catalpa; 9. sumac; 10. elderberry; 11. evergreen; 12. chestnut.

**It's on a Penny**

With a little imagination and perserverence all of these things may be found on a Lincoln Head Penny.

1. a fruit                    _____
2. top of a hill              _____
3. large body of water        _____
4. a beverage                 _____
5. a rabbit                   _____
6. a messenger                _____
7. a flower                   _____
8. part of corn               _____
9. railroad track part        _____
10. part of a needle          _____
11. portion of a river        _____
12. a sacred place            _____

ANSWERS:   1. date; 2. brow; 3. sea (c); 4. tea (t); 5. hare (hair); 6. one sent (cent);
7. tulips (two lips); 8. ear; 9. tie; 10. eye; 11. mouth; 12. temple.

## Maximizing Social Interaction

The following tips may prove useful in the process of stimulating interaction when leading activities with older adults.

- Welcome each person as he/she enters the room.
- Greet each one by name making sure that the leader and client make eye contact.  It often helps to shake hands.
- Introduce clients to the others to help them remember names.  Having clients introduce themselves will help reinforce other clients' names.

## Resources

Bettmann, O. L.  (1974).  *The Good Old Days - They were Terrible.*  New York, NY:  Random House, Inc.

Feldman, D. (1987).  *Why do Clocks Run Clockwise?  And Other Imponderables.*  New York, NY:  Harper and Row Publishers.

*The Game of Games.*  Madison, WI:  Bi-folkal Productions, Inc.

Merrill, T. (1974).  *Discussion Topics for Oldsters in Nursing Homes.*  Springfield, IL:  Charles C. Thomas Publishers.

Panat, C. (1987).  *Extraordinary Origins of Everyday Things.*  New York, NY:  Harper and Row Publishers.

Seymour, J. (1984).  *The Forgotten Crafts.*  New York, NY:  Alfred A. Knopf, Inc.

Sloane, E. (1964).  *A Museum of Early American Tools.*  New York, NY:  Random House, Inc.

Sloane, E. (1955).  *Our Vanishing Landscape.*  New York, NY:  Random House Inc.

# CHAPTER 12

# WORKING WITH THE CONFUSED CLIENT

**Using Repetitive Tasks**

**Working With Wanderers**

**Familiar Activities**

**Reminiscence Activities**

**Sensory Activities**

**Environmental Orientation**

**Resources**

# WORKING WITH THE CONFUSED CLIENT

It would be so nice to have a step by step approach to working with the confused and disoriented client. However each client is an individual and comes to the facility with a different background. Therefore, even if something works with one client it will not necessarily work with another. Many of the activities from the previous two chapters will work well with the client who is confused and disoriented with little or no adaptation. This chapter is a compilation of ideas and approaches for working with these very special clients.

In recent years there has been a tendency to label all of these clients as having Alzheimer's Disease. In many cases this may be an appropriate label, but in others the cause might be depression, medications or other diseases. Without special medical training it is impossible for the recreation personnel to determine the cause of the confusion, therefore they must work with the symptons.

Researchers have found that the client first loses orientation to time and place, then recognization of people, then the ability to count and finally his/her own name. The recreation professional should work with the abilities the clients have in an attempt to challenge the client to keep striving. Providing an environment where achievement is possible is extrememly important when working with the confused client.

If a client has already lost orientation to time and place, then work on skills which are still familiar such as math, spelling, and reading. If a client has lost orientation to time, continue to work on the orientation to place. If a client has lost the ability to count, continue to work on those skills such as eating, and dressing as well as the sensory stimulation skills. If a client is exhibiting no response at all, attempts should be made to solicite a reponse to his/her name.

## Using Repetitive Tasks

Often clients who are confused exhibit great frustration and restlessness. The idea of focusing on the skills they do have, is to give the client a focus which is positive in nature. Often clients who wander and make a lot of noise, or are constantly asking where their room is located, can often be distracted for short periods with familiar, repetitive tasks. Even though their attention is focused on the task for very short periods their energies can be rechanneled many times with the same task.

Confused clients often seem worried and fretful over the same problem. It may be to find their room or to get home in time to cook a meal for their "small" children. Refocusing their efforts gives them something else to think about (even if it is temporary), provides them with a sense of purpose and can help them stay calm.

It is almost impossible to calm a client down with a repetitive task once he/she has become agitated. The challenge for the staff is to asign a task before the client reaches a state of agitation. Although it would be nice to assign all of the confused clients a repetitive type task, the idea does not work for all of the clients. However, it does work for many and should be utilized when possible. The best types of tasks would include those which are familiar or comfortable.

For example, dusting or folding towels often works well with many women. Sorting old style computer punch cards or other types of cards by color has also been found to be helpful. The client must feel the task is helping the staff. It will not be effective if the client realizes the cards are being reshuffled or clothes unfolded.

These repetitive tasks have been used successfully:

- dusting handrails and/or table tops
- polishing shoes or silverware
- sorting silverware
- washing table tops
- folding laundry or towels
- sorting cards by color or size
- rolling embroidery thread onto cards
- rolling yarn into balls

## Working With Wanderers

Many of the clients who enter the facility exhibiting signs of confusion are still able to walk and take care of their daily needs. However, they do not like to stay in the facility and often become the "wanderers." In the past, the solution has been to use restraints. Restraining keeps the clients from wandering, but almost always results in their deterioration to the point of no response. There is a movement in an increasing number of states to prohibit the use of restraints in elder care facilities. Many facilities have begun to move toward a restraint-free envionment even though it is not yet required. In one agency the nursing assistant assigned to the client takes the client on a short walk around the grounds, or inside the facility, upon the client's request. They report having to take some clients on two or three walks per hour in those late afternoon and early evening hours, which are so common for *escape* attempts. When the client realizes a walk can be taken anytime, less walks are required. The client will often sit calmly and wait until the staff member is free from other tasks to take the walk. Recreation personnel can certainly join with the nursing staff to assist with a walking program. Since it is often difficult to gather a group of clients for late afternoon activities. This would be a perfect time of day to take a client or two for a stroll around the grounds.

Many agencies with clients who wander seem to be afraid to take the client outside the facility for fear the client will try to escape at a later time. It is difficult to argue with this logical thinking however, after observing client after client go downhill because they were forced to give up the one activity which seemed to give them joy, a walk upon the client's request appears worth a try.

A solution which worked for one agency was to install large red stop signs (similar to those used on highways) on all exterior doors. Even the most confused wanderer responded to this familiar symbol from the past by turning and walking in another direction.

Other solutions include alarms on exterior doors or electronic locators worn by the wandering clients.

## Familiar Activities

If the client cannot tell the recreation professional about leisure interests, then family members should be consulted. Often familiar activities can serve as a tool to achieve success with the confused client. For example, a client who wanders the hall constantly looking for her room might happily re-pot plants with the recreation person because she always liked to garden. Another person labeled as a wanderer might happily join in a bridge game with fellow clients and play extremely well.

Activities such as spelling bees, name the tune, finish the proverb, and simple math problems utilizing long-term memory skills are very successful with the clients. They are familiar skills which take little or no short-term memory on the client's part and give the client a sense of accomplishment when they remember the correct answer.

## Reminiscence Activities

Reminiscence sessions about life in the early days, including such aspects as school, crafts, household tasks, and going to the market, work extremely well. The staff does not need to know all of the details about life in the old days as the clients will supply the details, but the staff member should certainly be interested. Family members might even bring in photographs from the past to utilize with the clients. The following list of activities provide similar reminiscence experiences.

- spelling bee
- math problems
- name the tune
- finish the proverb
- What is It? Identify old household items and tools and demonstrate their usage.
- Concentration or Matching Game—with either memory game cards, "Skip-Bo" cards or a playing deck. Have clients see if they can match two cards. They get an extra turn for every matched pair. For a more advanced group or individual, play with the cards face down on the table. For a less advanced group, play with the cards face up. For a very low level client play with only four cards and try to work toward a greater number.
- Categories—take a person's name and have the group or individual identify as many new words as possible that start with that same initial. For example, Judy-jelly, jump, joy

## Sensory Activities

A few of the sensory activities from the previous chapter will be applicable for use with confused and disoriented clients. The following sensory activities have been used successfully with these clients.

- Rub client's skin with vaious textures such as corduroy.
- Use hand gestures to act out hello, stop, thin, tall, etc.
- Have the client clap hands, reach out, make a fist, laugh, smile, frown, etc.
- Ooh, Aah—squeeze the hand of the person on the right and say "ooh," squeeze the hand on the left and say "aah." This works best with group seated in a circle.
- Play tape recording of people laughing, crying, clapping, etc., and see if client can make up a story or identify the action.
- Who Am I?—Ask client to identify people by name.
- Ball pass—pass different size and textures of balls, squeeze the ball as well as passing, tossing and kicking actions.
- Bounce the ball—have clients count the number ot times the ball is bounced.
- Body movement exercises—use the game "Simon Says" to do exercises such as lift arms over head, etc.
- Telephone—using a lightweight telephone, see if the person will attempt to answer the phone.
- Play a variety of short songs on a walk-a-long radio near the client's ear.

## Environmental Orientation

Providing a supportive enviornment which encourages the person to achieve as much as possible is probably the single most imortant factor for working with these clients. The client should be approached in a manner which encourages a response. Simple decisions should be encouraged whenever possible. If nothing is expected of the client then there will be no response. Everyone needs to feel some purpose in their lives and these clients often seem to have given up. As less and less is expected, the clients lose more and more of their identity until there is no response at all to stimuli. The idea is to go in the direction of restoration, even though total restoration may be impossible. The client should always be approached in an adult manner.

Imagine how upsetting and frustrating it must be to realize that you have no idea which way to turn in order to find your room. Or, you don't know the date. Now imagine being able to complete a puzzle or remember a cookie recipe, especially since there are so many things you can not remember. The sense of pride and accomplishment at being able to succeed at a task is vital to the client's health. The recreation personnel should do everything possible to provide a successful experience and environment for the client.

## Resources

Bettman, O. L. (1974) *The Good Old Days—They were Terrible*. New York, NY: Random House, Inc.

Merrill, T. (1967). *Activities for the Aged and Infirm*. Springfield, IL: Charles C. Thomas Publishers.

# CHAPTER 13

# EXERCISE AND THE OLDER ADULT

**Benefits Of Exercise**

**Participation Concerns**

**Tips For Exercising With Older Adults**

**Exercises For The Older Adults**

**Exercise Set To Music**

**Scheduling Exercise Programs**

**Resources**

# EXERCISE AND THE OLDER ADULT

This section will explore the usage of exercise for the older adult. Included will be the benefits of exercise as well as tips for motivating the clients and keeping the exercise program exciting. Sample exercises are included.

Exercise has become more important to Americans in the past several years as scientists report the various benefits of exercising. The older person has received some of this attention with books exclusively for this population. This chapter can not begin to present all of the material on exercise and the older adult, therefore, recommended books on exercise and the older adult are included.

## Benefits Of Exercise

Older adults who exercise on a regular basis report an overall sense of well-being. They often comment about how much easier it is to go about their daily tasks since they have begun exercising. They also express an increased flexibility in their movements. Exercise can give the clients a personal sense of achievement as they feel they have made progress.

Exercise programs should be part of the regularly scheduled recreation program because the clients often experience such a wonderful sense of satisfaction. The recreation staff must remember that exercise can take on many forms and should not be limited to traditional calisthenics. Activities such as volleyball, bowling, gardening and walking provide a great amount of exercise and should be considered as part of the clients' exercise program. Even within the traditional exercise program props such as hats, scarves, canes, and balls can help motivate the older adult to exercise.

The term "exercise" is often a "turn-off" to the residents. Renaming the program will often make the activity attractive to more individuals. Titles such as "Stoop and Stretch," "Men's Sweat," Flexercise" or "Aerobics" (although it is almost impossible to achieve aerobic action with this population) have been used.

As with any recreational activity some clients will easily join in and others will want to sit along the side lines. It is important to encourage the client to 'come and watch' if the client does not wish to actively participate. Older adults are often leery about trying new activities and exercise is something they often consider would be difficult. After a few observations, most clients will be willing and able to participate in the activity.

## Participation Concerns

Older adults are often concerned with their health and afraid to try exercising because of possible injury. Instead of thinking about how beneficial exercise can be for them they shy away from the activity. Giving them the opportunity to watch the group often eliminates their concern.

Recreation professionals have expressed the concern that the older adult might over-exercise and cause themselves injury. The chances of the older adult overextending themselves are slim as older adults have an amazing ability to pace themselves. Often the reverse is true and the recreation person will have to encourage the older adult to try harder.

Aerobic actions should not be the goal of exercise for older adults. Maintenance of muscle tone and flexibility are the two benefits of an exercise program.

## Tips For Exercising With Older Adults

- Arrange the group in a semicircle formation with enough room between each person. This formation is familiar and comfortable.
- Always face the group. Not only will it be easier to observe their efforts, but they will feel more comfortable.
- Eliminate the concept of right and left. It really doesn't matter which side they do first, just so they do both sides.
- Allow extra time for each movement since the clients' reaction time is slower than a younger person. Each set of movements should be a minimum of sixteen counts.
- Avoid coordinated movements which require the usage of arms and legs together. Since coordinated movements are difficult for the client they will tend to work only one body part and that is usually the arms.
- If some of the clients are standing while they exercise, have a chair in front of them for extra security. Knowing they can grab onto the back of the chair helps the client to feel more secure; therefore, they will work harder.
- Use images whenever possible to encourage the clients to remember the movement. For example, arms up high with fingers wiggling as the arms lower down can be called "rain." Arms crossing in front of the body as they rise to form a circle and lower back down can represent the sun bursting through the clouds.
- Clients should be encouraged to recognize movements, but not to memorize routines. It may take clients several weeks to learn a sequence of movements which cuts down on the benefit of their exercise program. Therefore, the instructor should prompt the client concerning the next movement.
- Add variety to the program when possible. Use props such as scarves, balls, hats, canes, and different music to add variety.
- Exercise with the clients a minimum of twenty minutes and a maximum of one hour several times a week. If the schedule does not permit time for more than two times a week then schedule another active program which would promote exercise, such as a walk.
- Avoid any bouncing, swinging, fast or rotating movements. Neck roles are not good for the older adult. Tilting the head back can cut off the blood supply to the neck and therefore should be avoided with this population. A replacement exercise is to turn the head slowly from side to side as if to say "no."
- Taking the pulse at the neck is not wise for this population. The pressure of the finger tips can quickly alter the heart rate making the client light headed. Therefore, the pulse should be taken at the wrist.
- Always exaggerate the movements in order to encourage the clients to complete the exercise.

- Do not correct a client if a movement is performed differently than demonstrated; almost any movement is more than the client would have done otherwise. Correct the movement if it is likely to cause the client injury.
- Have fun while exercising with the clients. The enthusiasm expressed by the leader is the key to client participation.
- Do a series of exercises for each part of the body including the face and working all the way down to the toes. *(Consult appropriate professionals before any program is initiated.)*
- Structure the program to include a warm-up period, a series of choreographed activities and a cool down period. The warm-up and cool-down may consist of stretching activities.
- If the clients are ambulatory, walking is one of the best forms of exercise. A walking club or program should be established to encourage older adults to exercise.

## Exercises For The Older Adults

As mentioned earlier, the best exercises for older adults are ones that they can easily follow. Associating an image with the exercise helps relieve boredom and helps the client remember the movement. A few suggestions follow.

**Sunburst** - cross both arms in front of chest, raise arms in a circular motion so they are above the head, slowly lower arms to side. Associate with the thought of the sun bursting through the clouds on a rainy day.

**Rain** - raise both arms above head and off to one side. Slowly lower arms to side while wiggling the fingers in a back and forth motion. This is great for improving the flexibility in the fingers. Raise arms and lower to the other side too.

**Birds** - raise both arms to side, slowly flap arms down and up to indicate a bird in flight.

**Waves** - arms in front of body slightly raised above hips. Sway back and forth with the arms moving in a horizontal figure eight. This should be done in slow motion.

**Ocean** - bend arms in front of the body so one arm is slightly higher than the other. The elbows should be bent. Rotate the arms in a circular motion as if to signify rolling water.

**Swim** - either do the front crawl or the back stroke while seated. Holding the nose and pretending to take a dip adds to the fun of this movement.

**Baseball** - act as the hitter getting ready to swing at the ball or the pitcher winding up to pitch. Switch sides and repeat.

**Basketball** - pretend to dribble the ball then reach up to shoot a basket. This can be done while seated, simply stretch the arms high and straighten the trunk of the body while making pretend shots.

**Jogging** - running in place, varying the speed from barely moving the feet to running quickly will make this exercise more fun for the clients.

**Kicking** - pretend to be on the beach making small kicks to move the water, or imagine being part of a fast paced soccer game in order to encourage the clients to kick. Pretending to be the Rockettes will also stimulate some high kicking.

**Smiles and Frowns** - this exercise can be done with either the wrists or ankles. Move the ankle in a circular motion making a half circle which looks like either a smile or a frown. Remember to do both movements.

**Picking Flowers** - bend down or reach forward as if to pick a flower off a bush. It is important to encourage clients to really reach for a flower. Using a grasping motion straighten up or return to a straight position, slowly bring the hands, still in a closed position, to the nose as if to smell the flower.

**Mowing the Lawn** - this image exercise is actually a series of movements which use both the upper and lower body. First pretend to drag the lawn mower out of the shed. Pull the cord to start the machine. Pretend it doesn't start the first time so the clients get some additional arm stretching. Walk along with the machine, even just pretending to walk while seated in a chair is great exercise for some clients. You can even make lawn mower noises which will work some of the facial muscles.

**Grocery Shopping** - this series of movements is extremely familiar and can also be used with all types of clients. Pulling the cart out from the other carts utilizes those upper body movements of stretching and reaching. Pretending to walk along and greet friends in the grocery store helps the lower extremities. Reaching for the can on the top shelf and raising on tip toe (even in a wheelchair, raise the heels off of the floor) and onto the bottom shelf for that heavy bag of dog food helps the clients forget they are exercising. This is a great way to exercise their mental abilities, as they reminisce about how to select grapefruit and other food items.

Following are examples of routines which have been choreographed to music for use with older adults. The routines may be adapted to fit the clients' needs.

## Exercise Set To Music

Movement images set to music add excitement to an exercise program and help the older adults forget they are exercising. Have fun with the images and include the clients in the process of creating new exercises.

**Uptown Girl**

"Uptown Girl"
Billy Joel
*An Innocent Man*
Columbia Records
New York, NY
QCT 38837

Introduction:

| | |
|---|---|
| Small twists side to side | 1 - 16 |

Step 1

| | |
|---|---|
| Show those muscles - two times | 1 - 8 |
| Punch the ceiling with right arm | 1 - 8 |
| Show those muscles - two times | 1 - 8 |
| Punch the ceiling with left arm | 1 - 8 |

Step 2

| | |
|---|---|
| Arm exercise-with fist | |
| Arms up | 1 - 2 |
| Arms open side | 3 - 4 |
| Arms lower down by side | 5 - 6 |
| Arms bend in | 7 - 8 |
| Repeat 3 more times | 1 - 24 |

Step 3

| | |
|---|---|
| Point forward right foot, left foot—continue for 16 counts | 1 - 16 |
| Shimmy right arm, lift it high | 1 - 4 |
| Shimmy left arm, lift it high | 5 - 8 |
| Repeat shimmy | 1 - 16 |

Step 4

Repeat step 3

Step 5

| | |
|---|---|
| Shoulder roll left 2 times | 1 - 8 |
| Shoulder roll right 2 times | 1 - 8 |
| Lasso right arm | 1 - 8 |
|     (lasso—circular motion with arm overhead) | |
| Lasso left arm | 1 - 8 |
| Repeat lasso | 1 - 16 |

Step 6

| | |
|---|---|
| Lift right leg straight off of the floor | 1 - 4 |
| Lift left leg straight off of the floor | 5 - 8 |
| Put the right leg back down | 1 - 4 |
| Put the left leg back down | 5 - 8 |
| Repeat above | 1 - 16 |

Step 7

| | |
|---|---|
| Pump iron 2 times | 1 - 8 |
| Pump iron 2 times | 1 - 8 |
|    (pump iron—lift arms in front of body to shoulder height, hands in a fist, and lower) | |
| Pump iron to full extension | 1 - 8 |
|    (raise arm above head as if holding a bar with weights) | |
| Repeat full extension | 1 - 8 |

Step 8

| | |
|---|---|
| Tri-cep stretch in front 2 times | 1 - 8 |
| Tri-cep stretch in front 2 times | 1 - 8 |
|    (tri-cep stretch—arms straight out to side, hands curled in fists, bend arms at elbows) | |
| Tri-cep stretch in back 2 times | 1 - 8 |
| Tri-cep stretch in back 2 times | 1 - 8 |
|    (tri-cep stretch in back—arms straight to side, hands in fists, palms facing floor.  Bend arms at elbows, so wrists are at waist level). | |

Step 9

| | |
|---|---|
| Shoulder roll left and right | 1 - 8 |
| Lasso right arm then left arm | 1 - 16 |
| Repeat lasso | 1 - 16 |

Step 10 and 11

Repeat step 6—leg lifts
Repeat step 7—pump iron
Pump iron to finish song

**It's Raining Again**

"It's Raining Again"
Supertramp
A&M Records
Hollywood, CA
AM-8646

Introduction

| | |
|---|---|
| Sway back and forth-windshield wiper arms | 1 - 32 |

    (windshield wipers—arms shoulder height, palms face out,
    fingers straight, move arms slightly to resemble car wipers)

Step 1

| | |
|---|---|
| Rain motion right, left | 1 - 8 |
| Slowly look left while frowning, smile at last count (look left) | 1 - 8 |
| Rain | 1 - 8 |
| Head tilts | 1 - 8 |

    (head tilt—slowly lower head to side as if to touch ear
    to shoulder, reverse)

Step 2

| | |
|---|---|
| Rain | 1 - 8 |
| Open both arms forward, waist height, palms to ceiling | 1 - 8 |
|    (friend motion) | |
| Rain | 1 - 8 |
| Lower head forward and recover | 1 - 8 |

Step 3

| | |
|---|---|
| One arm open forward, palm up | 1 - 4 |
| Other arm open forward, palm up | 1 - 4 |
| Raise both arms up to ceiling, back of wrists touch | 1 - 4 |
| Arms lower to side | 1 - 4 |
| Repeat above | |

Step 4

| | |
|---|---|
| Rain | 1 - 8 |
| Look left | 1 - 8 |
| Rain | 1 - 8 |
| Friend motion | 1 - 8 |

Step 5

| | |
|---|---|
| Tap step front (4 times) | 1 - 16 |

    (tap ball of foot forward, return to place, tap other
    foot forward)

| | |
|---|---|
| Tap step side to side (4 times)<br>(same as above, except to the side) | 1 - 16 |

## Step 6

| | |
|---|---|
| Fighter<br>(hands in fists, punch, alternating arms as if boxing) | 1 - 24 |
| Sunburst | 1 - 8 |

## Step 7

| | |
|---|---|
| Rain | 1 - 8 |
| Look left | 1 - 8 |
| Rain | 1 - 8 |
| Friend motion | 1 - 8 |

## Step 8

| | |
|---|---|
| Tap step front (4 times) | 1 - 16 |
| Tap step side to side (4 times) | 1 - 16 |

## Step 9

| | |
|---|---|
| Torso twists (eight times)<br>(Hands on waist, turn to one side, return center and<br>turn to other side, slowly) | 1 - 32 |

## Step 10

| | |
|---|---|
| Fighter | 1 - 24 |
| Sunburst | 1 - 8 |
| Break<br>(sway to music) | |
| Sunburst | 1 - 8 |
| Large sunburst bending at waist | 1 - 8 |

## Step 11

| | |
|---|---|
| Tap step front (4 times) | 1 - 16 |
| Tap step side to side (4 times) | 1 - 16 |

## Step 12

| | |
|---|---|
| Torso twists (eight times) | 1 - 32 |

## Step 13

| | |
|---|---|
| Rain | 1 - 8 |
| Look left | 1 - 8 |
| Rain | 1 - 8 |
| Friend motion | 1 - 8 |

|                                        |        |
|----------------------------------------|--------|
| Rain                                   | 1 - 8  |
| Head tilts                             | 1 - 8  |
| Rain until end of music                |        |

## Million Dollar Baby

"I Found A Million Dollar Baby
(In a Five & Ten Cent Store)"
Barbra Streisand
*Funny Lady*
Artists Records
New York, NY
AL 9004

Introduction

|                                        |        |
|----------------------------------------|--------|
| Hold                                   | 1 - 16 |

Step 1

|                                                              |        |
|--------------------------------------------------------------|--------|
| Tap step                                                     | 1 - 8  |
| Kick step                                                    | 1 - 8  |
| Step forward right foot, then left foot, arms forward        | 1 - 2  |
| Step back in place right, left, arms lower                   | 1 - 2  |
| Repeat step forward and back                                 | 1 - 4  |
| Heel drops                                                   | 1 - 8  |
|     (lift and lower heels to floor alternately) |  |

Step 2

|                                        |        |
|----------------------------------------|--------|
| Repeat Step 1                          | 1 - 32 |

Step 3

|                                                                      |       |
|----------------------------------------------------------------------|-------|
| Arms open to V over-head and lower                                   | 1 - 8 |
| Palms open, small circular motion with arms in front of body        | 1 - 8 |
| Arms open to V over-head and lower                                   | 1 - 8 |
| Palms open, small circular motion with arms in front of body        | 1 - 8 |

Step 4

|                                        |        |
|----------------------------------------|--------|
| Touch ball of foot, lower heel         | 1 - 2  |
| Reverse and continue                   | 3 - 32 |

Step 5

|                                        |        |
|----------------------------------------|--------|
| Tap step                               | 1 - 8  |
| Kick step                              | 1 - 8  |

| | |
|---|---|
| Step forward right, left, arms forward | 1 - 2 |
| Step back in place right, left, arms lower | 1 - 2 |
| Repeat step forward and back | 1 - 4 |
| Heel drops | 1 - 8 |

### Step 6

| | |
|---|---|
| Tap step | 1 - 8 |
| Kick step | 1 - 8 |
| Step forward right, left, arms forward | 1 - 2 |
| Step back in place right, left, arms lower | 1 - 2 |
| Repeat step forward and back | 1 - 4 |
| Heel drops | 1 - 8 |
| Step, step, step, touch top of toe on floor, palms up in a shrug motion | 1 - 8 |

## New York  New York

"Theme from New York New York"
Frank Sinatra
Reprise Records
GRE0122
(XNY21035)

### Part I

Introduction

| | |
|---|---|
| Drop heels, slap knees | 1 - 16 |

### Step 1

| | |
|---|---|
| Tap step front | 1 - 16 |
| Heel toe, step in place right, left, right | 1 - 8 |
| Reverse heel toe | 1 - 8 |
| (Heel toe, step, lift foot to touch heel on floor, ball of foot raised, touch top of toe on floor, step full foot to floor) | |

### Step 2

| | |
|---|---|
| Heel step | 1 - 16 |
| Heel toe, heel toe, heel toe, step right, left, right | 1 - 16 |
| Reverse heel toe | |
| | 1 - 16 |

### Step 3

| | |
|---|---|
| Kick step | 1 - 16 |
| Jump legs apart and closed, crossing one leg over the other (4 times) | 1 - 16 |

Step 4

    Shuffle step                                         1 - 16

        (Shuffle—in a swinging motion, brush ball of foot as
        foot swings forward, and ball of foot on floor as foot
        swings back)

    Heel toe, heel toe, heel toe, step right, left, right     1 - 16

Step 5

    Reverse Step 4                             1 - 32

    Tap step                                     1 - 8

Step 6

    Kick step                                   1 - 8

    Both arms lift high and lower              1 - 8

    Repeat kicks                            1 - 16

    Repeat both arms high and lower          1 - 8

    Break

    Both arms high                            1 - 4

    Both arms slowly lower to side            1 - 4

    Little circle with arms in front of body, palms open   1 - 8

    Part II
    (Slower than Part I)

Step 7

    Kick across other leg and un-cross (4 times)      1 - 16

    Arms high and lower (2 times) slowly       1 - 16

Step 8

    Kick step (8 times)                     1 - 16

    Arms push forward and back (2 times), tiny steps with feet  1 - 16

    Kick step (8 times)                     1 - 16

        (Hold)

    Hands in fist push both arms to ceiling

## Bless the Beasts and Children

"Bless the Beasts and Children"
Barry De Vorzon and Perry Botkin, Jr.
A & M Records
AM-08602

Introduction

    Hold                                      1 - 16

Step 1

| | |
|---|---|
| Arms lift in front of body, slowly open and lower to sides | 1 - 8 |
| Repeat above | 1 - 8 |
| Right arm lifts from side gracefully to over-head and lowers | 1 - 4 |
| Left arm lifts from side gracefully to over-head and lowers | 1 - 4 |
| Both arms lift over-head from sides, touch back of wrists together | 1 - 4 |
| Repeat both arms lift, lower very slowly | 1 - 8 |

Step 2

| | |
|---|---|
| Right arm forward and open to side (friend motion) | 1 - 4 |
| Left arm forward and open to side (friend motion) | 1 - 4 |
| Both arms forward, palms up as if reaching out to friends | 1 - 4 |
| Both arms lift over-head from sides, touch back of wrists together | 1 - 4 |
| Repeat both arms lift, lower very slowly | 1 - 8 |

Step 3

| | |
|---|---|
| Stretch leg out to side as arm stretches forward in a circular motion | 1 - 8 |
| Reverse | 1 - 8 |
| Repeat above | 1 - 16 |
| Sunburst—raise arms and lift legs off of floor | 1 - 8 |

Step 4

| | |
|---|---|
| Arms lift in front of body, slowly open and lower to sides | 1 - 8 |
| Repeat above | 1 - 8 |
| Right arm lifts from side gracefully to over-head and lower | 1 - 4 |
| Left arm lifts from side gracefully to over-head and lower | 1 - 4 |
| Lift both arms to over-head from sides, | 1 - 8 |

Step 5

| | |
|---|---|
| Right arm forward and open to side | 1 - 4 |
| Left arm forward and open to side | 1 - 4 |
| Both arms reach forward and open | 1 - 4 |
| Lift both arms to overhead from sides | 1 - 4 |
| Repeat both arms overhead very slowly then bow | 1 - 8 |

## Scheduling Exercise Programs

An exercise program scheduled to meet three times per week forever, is likely to make the clients lose interest. It is better to schedule the program in six to eight week sessions. The clients are more willing to commit themselves for this time period. At the end of six to eight weeks, they can be given certificates to show that they have completed "Exercise I." "Exercise II" can begin the next week and run for another six to eight weeks.

There are many activities available to promote exercise. Clients should be encouraged to participate in a variety of activities. The next chapter has additional activity ideas which promote exercise.

## Resources

Alter, J. (1983). *Surviving Exercise.* Boston, MA: Houghton Mifflin Company.

Anderson, B. (1980). *Stretching.* Bolinas, CA: Shelter Publishing.

Basmajian, J. V. MD. (1983). *Therapeutic Exercise.* Malabar, FL: Robert E. Krieger Publisher.

Bender, R. (1976). *Be Young and Flexible After 30, 40, 50, 60...* Avon, CT : Riben Publishing.

Biegel, L. (1984). *Physical Fitness and the Older Person.* Rockville, MD: Aspen Publication.

Corbin, D. E. and Corbin-Metal, J. (1983). *Reach For It.* Dubuque, IA: Eddie Bowers Publishing Company

Erdman, M. (1984). *Undercover Exercise.* Englewood Cliffs, NJ : Prentice-Hall.

Garnet, E. D. (1982). *Movement Is Life.* Princeton, NJ : Princeton Book Company.

Godfrey, C. and Feldman, M. (1984). *The Ageless Exercise Plan.* New York, NY: McGraw-Hill.

Parker, B. (1983). *Sit Down and Shape Up.* New York, NY : Leisure Press.

Rockwell, R. E. and Osbourne, N. E. (1984). *Fitness and Nutrition for Seniors.* Springfield, IL: Charles C. Thomas.

Rosenberg, M. (1977). *Sixty Plus and Fit Again.* New York, NY: M. Evans and Company, Inc.

Ross, M. A. (1984). *Fitness for the Aging Adult with Visual Impairment.* New York, NY: American Foundation for the Blind.

Sullivan, J. V. (1984). *Fitness for the Handicapped.* Springfield, IL: Charles C. Thomas.

Winnick, J. P. and Short, F. X. (1985). *Physical Fitness Testing.* Champaign, IL: Human Kinetics.

# CHAPTER 14

# ACTIVITIES THAT PROMOTE EXERCISE

**Recreational Walking**

**Familiar Indoor Activities**

**Outdoor Activities**

**Sports-Related Activities**

**Wheelchair Activities**

**Marble Board Games**

**Scheduling Suggestions**

**Resources**

# ACTIVITIES THAT PROMOTE EXERCISE

Many people do not like to exercise alone. For this reason most people, including the elderly, do not get enough physical activity. Because older people tend to tire easily, they often do not think they should exercise. The activities presented in this section promote physical activity at a comfortable level for the older person. The activities are familiar, can be done with other clients, and include adaptations which have been used successfully with this population.

## Recreational Walking

Walking is good exercise for the elderly, however, if confined to a wheelchair, self-locomotion can provide excellent exercise also. The problem is that as a person becomes older and locomotion of any kind becomes more difficult, there is a tendency to do as little as possible unless there is a good reason. Walking back and forth in the hallways becomes boring very quickly. Two things can be done to encourage self-locomotion as a way to get exercise. The first is to give the individual a reason for doing it and the second is to provide a place for the clients to do it.

### Walking Area Design

Facility plans should include an area for the clients to walk. Unfortunately, most facility designers only plan an open area, such as a patio, and feel that this is enough space. A walking area does not have to be long, but it should provide a circular route so the people walking can do more than walk back and forth.

The walkway may begin at a patio and preferably have a few gentle curves which take the client through a variety of areas which include plantings, garden plots, and flower beds. The walkway should end near where it began so the client can easily find his/her way back into the facility. The walkway should be level with benches for resting. It may be desirable to have the area enclosed with a fence or landscaped with vegetation so the confused client cannot wander away.

The walkway will provide many hours of enjoyment for the clients and a number of different recreation programs can be offered utilizing the area. Even frail clients could enjoy the area in their wheelchairs, if the walkway is level and paved.

### Walk Around the Country

This on-going program should encourage the participation of both staff and residents. The object is to build up the mileage that would be needed to walk from one major national attraction to another. When that attraction has been "reached" a program is presented featuring that destination. A large map is kept with the route marked and the distance updated each week.

The first step is to introduce the idea and get the clients' input as to places they would like to "visit." Lay out the route to be taken and record the distances to be walked to get from one destination to the next. Outline the route on a large wall map, making sure the first several destinations are not more than 15 or 20 miles apart. The next step is to measure the length of the hallways and walkways around the facility. Make a chart that easily converts these distances into decimal portions of a mile.

Set up a publicity program which includes all departments. Encourage all of the staff to actively participate in the walking program. Get across the idea that only recreational walking/biking counts. Going to meals, driving to work and work-related walking do not count. Walking to work (instead of driving), riding a bicycle, and walking for exercise all count.

Provide charts for recording distances walked at various locations, such as nurses' stations or lounges. It will take some encouragement to get the project going and some reminders to record the distances travelled. Designate certain people (clients, if possible) to record the mileage and add it to the master list. Remember, whether the person walks unaided, uses a wheelchair, or another assistive device, it all counts. Pledges to walk a certain distance every day should be encouraged.

When each destination is reached have a special program relating to the place. Such a program could be a slide show, a speaker, or theme party. Often some food specialty from the place can be prepared. Keep the staff and clients informed as to the mileage gained each week, the total mileage to date, and the distance needed to reach the next destination.

One facility that used the program called it "Walk-Around-The-World" and the clients have "visited" many exciting places with the program.

## Familiar Indoor Activities

These familiar indoor activities have been adapted for use with older people. They can be used outside during warm weather and inside the rest of the year. They can be competitive or played without keeping score. Either way, the clients receive the benefits of physical activity while having fun.

### Volleyball

A regular volleyball is too difficult for the clients to use. It is too small, too heavy and too hard. A small light-weight beach ball is a much better choice. For an even lighter ball, use an inflatable punch ball, or a balloon. To make the balloon a little heavier, use a double balloon (one inside the other). To prepare a double balloon insert the eraser end of a pencil in an uninflated balloon. Use the pencil to insert this balloon into the second balloon and remove the pencil. Inflate both balloons at the same time and tie them securely. The result is a double-walled balloon that is heavier and sturdier than a single balloon.

An inexpensive badminton net may be used. Make it more visible by inserting fluorescent flagging tape along the top of the net. A serviceable net may be made from a length of nylon rope to which 2 foot flagging tape streamers have been attached. Four foot broomsticks can be tied or taped to chair backs to support the net 3 1/2 or - 4 feet above the floor or patio. Mark off the playing area approximately 10 x 20 feet using two-liter plastic containers at the corners.

Two rows of three players on each side of the net (12 participants) is about the right number for this size court. Each player is seated in a chair (or wheelchair) facing the net. The server is any person in the front row.

The ball is tossed over the net by the server and caught by an opposing team member who must toss it to one other team member before it is returned over the net. If the ball touches the floor before it gets back over the net it is a point for the serving team. Rotate the serve from team to team not worrying about "losing the serve" as in a regulation game. Play for a score of six. Veteran volleyball players will recognize that most of these rules are adapted from the game called "Newcomb."

## Quoit Golf

Regular golf is too strenuous for some older adults. Trips to a nearby miniature golf course has possibilities for those ambulatory clients that can negotiate such a course. Construction of a readily accessible course at a residential facility should not be considered for both space and cost reasons.

Quoit golf is an inexpensive substitute which will provide some of the excitement and exercise elements of regular golf. It can be played indoors or outside, is adaptable to a wide range of abilities, and is quickly set up and easily stored.

Six #10 cans (ask the dietary department for them) and three two-pound coffee cans are needed for a nine hole course. The coffee cans are used for three holes because they fit inside the larger cans so that everything can be stored in the six-can carton in which the large cans come.

Cover each of the nine cans with bright yellow or orange contact paper to make them easy to see. Use a black magic marker or large vinyl numbers to designate the cans from 1 to 9 (The smaller cans should be 7, 8 and 9). Rope quoits (4 inch circles of 3/8 inch rope) are best for the game, however bean bags could be used.

Directions for making the quoits are found in the chapter on MAKING THINGS (pages 153, 154).

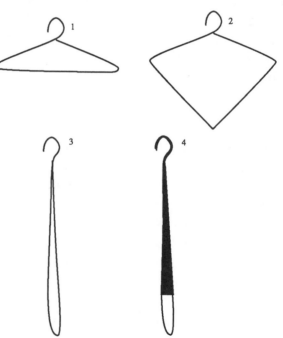

**Figure 13**   Retrievers

To help those individuals who cannot stoop to pick up a quoit, make "retrievers" from coat hangers. Leaving the hook as is, straighten the hanger to make a double wire as long as possible. Wrap the double wire with tape to make a handle as shown in the accompanying sketch [Figure 13].

Put a little tape on the end of the hook to protect the point. Players can carry the "retriever" with them to pick up the quoits.

To prepare for playing, place the cans around an open grassy area, or even on the patio, at a distance which will require the player to toss from the "tee," walk to the quoit, pick it up and toss it again, and repeat this action at least a third time to toss the quoit into the next can (this is a par 3 hole).

The game is usually played in "threesomes," using colored tape to mark the quoits so each person can easily identify his/her quoit. After one group of three has "holed out," and is ready to move to the next hole, another group can start.

Each player has a score card with the numbers "1" through "9" down one side. Upon completion of a hole, each player marks down the number of strokes (tosses) it took for that hole next to the number on the score card. The final score for each player is found by totaling the number of strokes for all nine holes. As in regular golf, a low score wins.

The distance between cans should be less when the game is first used so that the players will experience success. In subsequent use, the distance between cans can be greater and there may be some obstacles placed between the cans to make it more of a challenge. This game is easily carried on outings and can be used many times during the year.

Following are several variations of the game which make it extremely versatile.

*Variation #1.* For clients who are not mobile, use one can with six or eight quoits. Place the container in front of the player and have the individual toss the quoits into the can. Move the can further away as the person's skill improves.

*Variation #2.* Place several cans in a large semicircle. Several clients seated in wheelchairs can play at the same time. Give each person several quoits to toss one at a time. When the player gets one in, he/she moves to the next can which is set at a greater distance. If players want to compete, they may keep track of how many they toss before "holing out."

*Variation #3.* Two individuals are seated facing each other about eight feet apart. A can is placed in front of each and the players are given an equal number of quoits. Each one tosses his/her quoits at the opponent's can. The winner of the round is the player who gets the most quoits in the other's can. Each person can use a retriever to collect the quoits within reach and the game is continued.

## Floor Soccer

This adaptation of soccer is played outdoors or inside with an eight-inch playball. All of the players are seated as shown in the diagram [Figure 14] and use their feet to move the ball toward the goal. Six players on each team provides an opportunity for all to be actively involved. Chairs should be about two feet apart in each row and facing players should be far enough apart that they can not accidentally kick each other. The goalie should have markers (two-liter soft drink cans partly filled with sand work well) about 18 inches on either side of his/her chair to designate the goal opening. Similar markers should be used to designate the corners of the playing area.

The leader tosses the ball into the middle and the play begins. Players may only use their feet to move the ball. The object is to propel the ball through the goal markers past the opposing goalie. If the ball goes out of bounds, the leader tosses it back into play at the spot where it was kicked out. Each time a

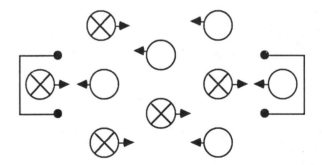

**Figure 14**  Floor Soccer Layout

goal is made, the leader tosses the ball back in the middle to start again. After each goal it is a good idea to have the players change positions. Each goal counts as two points and the team to get six points first is the winner.

This activity has a great amount of leg exercise and care should be taken to ensure players do not become excessively fatigued.

## Broom Hockey

This game is suitable for six to eight players.  An old broom is needed for each person and to propel the 6 inch playball toward the goal.  Alternate the players in each line as shown in the diagram [Figure 15] and use two chairs to mark the goal lines on either end.

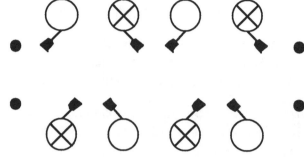

The players chairs should be about 2 feet apart in the lines and the lines should be about 5 feet apart.

To play, the leader drops the ball in the middle and each person uses his/her broom to move the ball to the goal on his/her left.  All players must remain seated in their chairs.  Each goal counts one point.  Set a timer for three to five minutes and when the buzzer sounds, the team with the highest score wins.

**Figure 15**   Broom Hockey Layout

## Bocci Ball

Bocci sets are available at most department stores, but the game can be played with tennis balls.  Although Bocci is traditionally played on an enclosed clay court the following adaptations can be made so that the game may be played either indoors on a carpeted floor or outside on a flat grassy area.

Each player is given a ball (tennis balls must be marked in such a way that the player can identify his/hers).  A smaller "jackball," about the size of a billiard ball, is rolled about 10 feet away from the semi-circle of players.  Each player rolls his/her ball in turn trying to have the ball stop rolling as close to the jackball as possible.  Rolling one's ball to knock the jackball away from another person's ball is permissible.

The ball closest to the jackball after all have rolled wins two points for its owner and the second closest ball receives one point.  A game is 11 points, or whatever total is decided upon.  The jackball may have to be painted a bright color so it may be easily seen.  The person with the highest score rolls out the jackball for the next round and is the first to roll his/her ball.  This gives the others a chance to roll their balls closer.

# Outdoor Activities

Many of the sports activities which were enjoyed in earlier years can be made available with little variation.  Even though some of these activities may not have been familiar to the clients before, learning and participating in them can provide hours of enjoyment.

## Horseshoes

Many of the men have played this game before. Many of the women will also enjoy it once they have learned to play. Rubber horseshoes are available but tend to mark the floor when played indoors. Since it was originally meant to be an outdoor game it is best played there. Most old time players dislike the light rubber horseshoes but are unable to handle the heavy regulation variety. Use the lighter "women's" horseshoes and space the pins 20 to 25 feet apart rather than the regulation 40 feet.

Score the game as in regular horseshoes (directions come with the set), except give a point to the closest shoe, even if it isn't a "ringer" or a "leaner." Read the rules and adapt them to the level of the individuals playing the game. It is suggested that the game be less than the regulation number of points, say six points, so that the players will not be too tired after the game.

## Croquet

Most of the clients will remember the game and will have played it in earlier years. It is often possible to have a croquet set donated to the department, so it isn't necessary to purchase one. Make sure a level lawn area is rolled with a heavy roller in the early spring and that the area is kept mowed, for the game is difficult to play on a rough lawn or in grass higher than one inch. Play in the early evening when the sun is low, or on hazy days making certain that the players are protected from sunburn and heat. Straw hats and sunscreen lotion are important considerations for any outdoor activity.

Certain adaptations will make the game easier for the clients to play. First, adapt the equipment by making the wickets larger. Use #9 galvanized wire purchased at a hardware store to make new wickets half again larger than those provided with the set. Then, using fluorescent flagging tape (also purchased at the hardware store), tie a bow to the top of each wicket and wrap flagging tape around the wire so it can be easily seen.

When laying out the playing area, place the wickets about two-thirds the regulation distance apart. Instead of two wickets in front of each end stake, use only one. This makes it possible for the player to hit the ball through the wicket and hit the stake in one stroke.

Several changes in the rules are helpful to speed up the game. Give each player two strokes per turn. If the ball goes through a wicket give the person an extra turn. Forget the other rules about hitting other balls, etc. The two rules are easily remembered by the clients and speed up the game considerably.

Shortening the handle on a mallet makes it possible to play the game from a wheelchair.

## Whiffleball

Whiffleball is a viable substitute for playing baseball with older adults. It may be a little difficult to schedule frequently, but one or two games a season between the clients and staff can be great fun for players and "fans." Bases, whiffleballs, bats and field liner can usually be borrowed from the community recreation department. Any smooth grassy area can serve as the playing field. The field should be lined as a baseball diamond, except the distance between bases should be no more than 25 feet. This gives the clients an opportunity to "run" without causing undue distress over how far it is to the base. The game should be scheduled for early morning or evening to avoid harmful effects from the sun.

Chairs should be available for the "fans" as well as the players. If insects are a problem, the area should be sprayed prior to the game. Insect spray should be kept on hand in case there are any persistent insects remaining.

Wheelchair clients as well as ambulatory individuals should be permitted to play. Two staff members should be available to help the hitter "run" the bases whether or not they are in a wheelchair. One of the two helpers should be in front of the wheelchair pulling so that the player will not feel like he/she is in danger of falling forward. Residents in wheelchairs usually feel more comfortable moving forward around the bases rather than being pulled backward.

If possible, have the administrator or director of nursing serve as the umpire. It adds to the excitement, and besides, what staff member would question a call? The staff team can be from any department, just ask for volunteers. There are a lot of staff members who will be willing to stay after work or even come in on their day off to get involved. The game should not last more than 45 minutes to an hour, even if only four or five innings are completed.

At first, special rules of five strikes per client may be necessary. After a few games, three strikes and three outs are possible. Clients should be encouraged to play all of the positions with volunteer "coaches" on the field assisting them.

## Lawn Bowling

This game is played like bocci ball which was described earlier. Use croquet balls for each participant and a billiard ball for the "jack ball." The game may be played on the area used for croquet. Following the rules used for bocci makes the game easy and fun to play.

## Sports-Related Activities

Eye-hand coordination is difficult for some older adults. Activities to improve this skill can be fun and stimulating. Since eye-hand coordination is also something that young children must learn, many pieces of sports equipment designed for children may be adapted for use with older adults. When selecting equipment, make sure the markings do not designate it as a child's toy.

## Ball Toss

It is difficult for many people to judge the speed and distance of a ball to be able to catch it. To make the task easier, place a tennis ball in a man's white work sock and tie a knot in the sock. When the ball is tossed, the sock slows the ball somewhat and is easily seen by the person to whom it is tossed. This trick will improve the chances that each person will make a successful catch. Tennis balls are useful for many activities and can often be obtained at no cost from tennis clubs which are happy to find a use for their "dead" balls.

## Batting Practice

Obtain a short fat plastic bat from the toy department of a discount store. A light easily seen ball, such as a nerf ball is usually included in the set. Seat the players in a semicircle with a suitable distance between them and give the bat to the first person. The short bat is easily held in one hand. The leader tosses the ball to the batter. After a couple of tries, the bat is given to the next person and the game continues.

## Tennis Practice

Short handled plastic rackets are also available in the toy section of discount stores. Two rackets, with large heads, and sponge rubber balls are usually in the set. It is unlikely that the clients will be able to hit the ball to each other, so give the rackets to two clients and have the leader toss the ball to each in turn. After a couple of turns the racquets can be given to other members of the group. Tennis practice makes a good small group activity.

# Wheelchair Activities

Clients in wheelchairs may participate in many of the above "sports" activities, however it is desirable to schedule some activities where all participants use wheelchairs. Ambulatory individuals should be encouraged to participate in such activities so that if the time comes they have to be confined to a wheelchair they will know how to maneuver. It also gives the people who are confined to wheelchairs an opportunity to excel.

These activities work well with small groups and may be combined to make a wheelchair obstacle course. The course makes a great addition to any type of "Olympic Games" program which is scheduled as a special event.

## Straight and Narrow

Place a 40-foot length of 2-inch tape on the floor or parking lot (remember to remove it immediately after the event or there will be trouble with the housekeeping department). Each participant must back the wheelchair the length of the line keeping a wheel on the tape.

Each person starts with 100 points and one point is subtracted each time the wheel goes off the line.

## Down the Alley

Make an alley 20 foot long and 2 inches wider than the outside width of the participant's wheelchair wheels. Use 4-inch boards laid parallel to mark the alley. Participants start with 100 points and lose two points each time a wheel touches the side of the alley. To increase the difficulty, have them back the wheelchairs through the space.

## Balloon Bust

Use masking tape to tape inflated balloons to the floor in a 20 by 20 foot area. Participants try to break as many balloons as possible by running over them with the wheels of their chairs. The participant receives five points for each balloon broken.

## Park It

Use six to eight one-liter plastic soft drink bottles to outline three sides of a "garage" space 2 inches larger than the wheelchair. Use a piece of masking tape to mark the front of the space. Participants must wheel down the "drive" at right angles to the "garage" and back into it. Time each participant and add 30 seconds for each bottle knocked over.

## Pass Under

Create a "bar" out of twisted crepe paper and fasten it to supports about 6 inches higher than the back of the wheelchair. The person in the wheelchair must pass under the obstacle by leaning forward while continuing to propel the chair under the bar. Score 10 points if successful.

## Other Obstacles

Other ideas might include wheeling the chair over an obstacle like a rug or up a slight incline. Three point turns between some boxes or a trip along a serpentine path can add excitement to an obstacle course. A little brainstorming will reveal many additional possibilities. Combine several of the ideas to make an obstacle course for an Olympic type competition.

# Marble Board Games

Many of the residents will remember playing "marbles" in their childhood. There are commercial games such as Chinese checkers and tic-tac-toe that are available and can be challenging to the participants. The marble board described below can easily be constructed by anyone with basic tools. Given the idea, a volunteer can usually be found to do the work. The board can be used for many games which take little concentration or skill, but will be challenging to the users.

## Board Construction

All of the dimensions are approximate and may be changed to fit the size of the scraps that are available. The base should be a 28 x 36 inch piece of 1/8 inch masonite. Cover it with a piece of short nap, closely woven carpet which is cemented in place. A one inch high edge made of 3/4 inch wood surrounding the board will keep the marbles on the playing surface. Sand all edges and corners to prevent injury to the users. Keep the board as lightweight as possible for ease of handling and make sure it is not wider than the tables on which it will be used.

Two movable ramps about 4 inches high with a slope that the marbles will roll down easily are made of 3/4 inch wood. Make two sides for each ramp from 1/8 inch masonite. The sides are a little higher than the ramp surface, to keep the marble on the ramp, but have the same configuration as the ramp. The back of the ramp hooks over the edge of the board and the front rests on the carpeted surface. [See Figure 16]

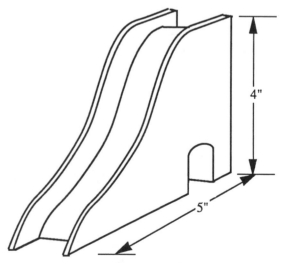

**Figure 16**  Ramp Design

It would be desirable to have four ramps so that four people can play at one time. All of the games may be played either crossways or longways on the board. It is better to start with short distances and increase them as the players skills increase.

## Marble Shooting

This is closest to the childhood game of marbles that clients may remember. Use narrow masking tape to make a five inch square in the middle of the board (making a circle with chalk might add more realism). Place four or five distinctively colored marbles in the circle as "counters." Players are on opposite sides of the board and have 10 marbles each. In turn, each player moves his/her ramp along the edge and releases one marble from the top of the ramp trying to force one of the "counters" out of the square. All marbles rolled are left where they land but the object of the game is to drive the ones that count points out of the square. One point is given to each player that forces one of the "counters" out of the square.

## Marble Football

Place a narrow strip of masking tape about 6 inches from each edge of the board where the ramps are located. Place a distinctive colored marble (the ball) equal distance from the lines (goals). Give each player an equal number of marbles (10 to 12). The game is to drive the "ball" across the opponent's goal by striking it with marbles rolled down the ramps. Each player picks up marbles, one at a time, and rolls them down the ramp trying to hit the ball. They do this as quickly as possible and when they run out of marbles they pick up marbles from the board that have rolled past the goal line on their side. A "touchdown" is scored when the "ball" is driven across the opponent's goal. Players often have to be reminded that they can slide the ramp along the edge of the board to get a better shot at the ball.

## Marble Bocci

This is a table form of the outdoor game played with marbles on the marble board. Place the "jack ball" (distinctive colored marble) near the edge of the board. All players use the same ramp from the opposite edge of the board from where the jack ball has been placed. Each player has a distinctively colored marble for ease of identification. The players each take a turn at rolling their marble down the ramp trying to get as close to the jack ball as possible. After each person has rolled his/her marble, the one closest to the jack ball wins two points for its owner and the next closest wins one point. The first person to get six points wins.

## Roll to a Line

This game is like the old game of pitching pennies. Place a line of narrow masking tape about two inches from the far edge of the board. Using different colored marbles, each person rolls one down the ramp trying to come close to the line but not go over it. Two points goes to the person nearest the line and one point to the second nearest.

**Table Tennis Ball**

The same board is used but discard the ramps and marbles. The activity is good to get the clients to use their lungs and breath more deeply. Give each player a large flexible drinking straw. Bend the short flexible end to a 45 degree angle with the long end to be placed in the player's mouth.

Line up a light Ping-Pong™ball in front of each player about two inches from the closest edge of the board. The object is to blow through the straw and try to force the ball to move toward the opposite edge of the board. The person on the other side tries to prevent it from touching the edge by using his/her straw to direct a blast of air to move the ball back across to the opposite edge. Score one point for each time a ball strikes an opponent's side.

Before playing this game each player should practice using the straw to direct a blast of air that will move a ball. The straws are used for two reasons. The first is that most clients will not be able to blow hard enough to move the ball unless the force is directed by the straw. Secondly, it makes the possibility of their losing their teeth in the excitement less likely!

Care should be taken that the activity is used for only a short period until clients are used to the additional use of their chest muscles, or the result may be hyperventilation and sore ribs.

## Scheduling Suggestions

Activities that promote exercise should be scheduled on a regular basis. Outdoor activities provide a welcome change and are well worth the extra time needed to schedule them and transport the clients. Some of the activities can be included in an Olympic type program and many others will serve as possible drop-in programs. Many of the events are designed for small groups and can be modified for larger groups or utilized on a 1:1 basis.

## Resources

Hinderman, D. (1978). *Kick the Can and Over 800 Other Active Games and Sports*. Englewood Cliffs, NJ: Prentice-Hall, Inc.

Parker, S. D., Will, C. and Burke, C. L. (1989) *Activities for the Elderly: A Guide to Quality Programming*. Owings Mills, MD: National Health Publishing.

# CHAPTER 15

# DANCING FOR SENIORS

Getting Started

Starter Dances

Breaks And Ending

Resources

# DANCING FOR SENIORS

Clients of all abilities can enjoy a dance experience.  They may only want to listen to the music or watch the action, but even wheelchair clients can participate in dancing with a little assistance from volunteers.  Whether the dance is part of an exercise group, a club, or a special event, the following notes should help the leader feel more prepared to provide a quality experience.

## Getting Started

If a large multi-purpose room is available, use it for dancing.  There will be many clients who come "just to watch," but this is the first step toward active participation.  If there is no large room available or even if there is one, consider having an outdoor dance in the parking lot some summer evening.

Arrange for enough volunteers and staff members so that each person in the dance will have a "pusher."  Remember that the "pusher" will be working all of the time, as different groups of dancers come on the floor.  Only the clients have a chance to rest, so choose volunteers who have the necessary strength and stamina.  Have a training session to orient the volunteers to the maneuvers.  It is a good idea to have it a few days  before the dance, rather than having them come early and trying to practice before the dance.  There are too many last minute things that need to be done to try to train the volunteers then.

### Adapting Dances

Be sure to pick simple dances.  Even then, it is often necessary to adapt the calls for the level of the clients.  Use records without calls, so the music can be slowed down enough to allow the dancers to finish an action before calling a new figure.  Round as well as square dances may be adapted for use with wheelchair clients.  Practice the calls ahead of time.  It is a good idea to select eight client volunteers and using regular volunteers, work out the dances before the program is initiated.

Use records on a variable speed record player rather than having them on tape.  This control allows one to not only change from 45 to 33 1/3 RPMs but also allows for variation of the speeds within those ranges.  The slower setting allows the leader to utilize a variety of dances which may otherwise be too fast.

Starting the dance in the middle of the record prevents the group from becoming extremely tired.  This is done by turning the volume control down before placing the needle onto the record.  Once the needle is in place, the volume control is turned back to the normal setting; or, the dance can be started at the beginning of the record and ended at the middle using the same technique.  In some situations, the group may need to do the dance several times before they recognize the movements.  This will depend on the group, and the leader needs to be sensitive to the group's needs.  Setting the speed control on the slower setting makes it easier to learn the dances.  Sometimes, it is even desirable to play a 45 RPM record at 33 1/3 RPM so the clients are able to participate.

## Program Suggestions

- Have the dance area set up ahead of time.  Know how large an area is needed for dancing and keep it clear.

- Have music playing when the clients arrive to help set the tone for the program.  Since there are usually more women, have hats for those taking the part of men while dancing.

- The clients who helped with the dance preparations should be the first on the floor to demonstrate how it is done.  Then others can be invited to participate.

- When the second group of participants is ready to dance, talk them through the figures so they will know what to expect.  Other groups that follow should receive the same treatment.

- It is a good idea to alternate a dance for the ambulatory with a wheelchair dance.  Be especially careful about mixing ambulatory and wheelchair clients in the same dance.  The wheelchair clients will run over the walkers because "they go so slow."

- Remembering older adults feel most comfortable with familiar activities, the leader should begin with movements which are familiar and simple.  A group sing or walk around the room to music are examples of familiar activities.

- Once the group has relaxed, begin with dances which take little to no instruction such as the "Hokey Pokey."

- Teach only one or two new movements per dance.  Through this method the clients learn new steps each dance, but are not overwhelmed by how long it takes to learn a dance.  They will be completing more difficult movements by the end of the dance if the dances build upon each other.

- Begin dances in the formation that the last dance ended with.  For example, if the dance ends in a circle, begin the next dance in a circle.  This saves time and avoids confusion.

- Partner and formation changes add variety to a dance.  Many dances known as mixers provide an opportunity to change partners.  A grand march is an excellent opportunity to change formations.

- Encourage both dancers and observers to clap in time to the music whenever possible.

- When a dance is finished, make sure the client is returned to his/her "spot."  It helps the client remain oriented to the action and avoids hurt feelings.


## Starter Dances

The following folk and novelty dances have been adapted for use with older clients.  They have been used successfully with both ambulatory and wheelchair clients.  Other dances may be adapted in the same manner for use with this population.

## Mixer

Music:     Worldtone 10034 x 45
           Patty Cake Polka

Formation: Circle of partners facing each other

| Call | Action |
|------|--------|

### Movement 1

| Call | Action |
|------|--------|
| • Heel and toe, heel and toe | Use forward foot,* touch heel to floor, then touch toe in front of other foot |
| • Slide, slide, slide, slide | Slide four steps counterclockwise around circle holding partner's hands |
| • Heel and toe, heel and toe | Use other foot for heel and toe |
| • Slide, slide, slide, slide | Slide four steps clockwise around circle holding partner's hands |

### Movement 2

| Call | Action |
|------|--------|
| • Right, right, right | Clap partner's right hand three times |
| • Left, left, left | Clap partner's left hand three times |
| • Both, both, both | Clap both hands of partner three times |
| • Knees, knees, knees | Hit own knees with hands three times |

### Movement 3

| Call | Action |
|------|--------|
| • Hook right arms and walk around | Link right elbows with partner and turn around |
| • And on to the next | Move to new partner on the left |

Repeat dance until end of music

*Ambulatory Variation*: Keep same partner throughout dance.

*Wheelchair Adaptation*: Single circle of chairs. (Movement 1) Tap right knee 2 times, turn chair to right and back. Tap left knee 2 times, turn chair to left and back. (Movement 2) Tap right chair arm 3 times, left 3 times, clap hands 3 times, slap knees 3 times. (Movement 3) Wheel to center and back to place.

* Forward foot—the foot closest to the direction the couple will move; in this case, clockwise.

**Mixer**

Music:    Windsor 4684 x 45
          Jiffy Mixer

Formation: Circle of partners facing each other.
           Inside person begins with left foot,
           outside person with right.

| Call | Action |
|------|--------|

**Movement 1**

- Heel and toe, heel and toe — Use forward foot,* touch heel to floor, then touch toe of same foot to floor

- Step together, step, close — Step counter clockwise with forward foot, close other foot to it, step again and close

- Heel and toe, heel and toe — Repeat above with other foot

- Step together, step, close — Repeat above going counterclockwise

**Movement 2**

- Hop, clap, hop, clap, hop, clap, hop, clap — Jump back from partner (count 1), clap (count 2). Repeat for a total of 4 hops

- Walk 2, 3, 4 — Four struts forward to new partner to left

Repeat to end of music

*Ambulatory Variation*: Use single circle facing center with no partners. Same actions but hop back then walk to place

*Wheelchair Adaptation*: Single circle facing center, no partners. (Movement 1) Tap chair arm twice, turn to right and back. Tap chair arm twice turn to left and back. (Movement 2) Pull chairs back while clients clap, then wheel forward.

* Forward foot—the foot closest to the direction the couple will move; in this case, clockwise.

**Novelty Dance**

Music:    Hi Hat  806 x 45
          Ding Dong Daddy

Formation:  Single circle facing center, no partners

| Calls | Action |
|---|---|
| **Movement 1** | |
| • Knees | Slap your knees twice |
| • Hands | Clap your hands twice |
| • Over | Palms down, cross right hand over left hand twice |
| • Under | Palms down, cross right hand under left hand twice |
| • Fists | Tap left fist with right fist twice |
| • Fists | Tap right fist with left fist twice |
| • Elbows | Tap right elbow with right fist two times |
| • Elbows | Tap left elbow with left fist two times |
| **Movement 2** | |
| • Swim, swim, swim, swim | Backstroke right arm, left arm, right arm, left arm |
| • Cheerleader | Raise arms and shout "yea." Do it twice |
| • Cowboy | Stand on right leg and swing "lasso" with left arm. |
| • Hitchhiker | Hitchhike "thumb" with right then left arm. |
| • Mosquito | Catch a mosquito with right hand, pat it in left and blow it away |

Repeat to end of music.

Adaptations:  This is a very fast dance.  It can be done standing or sitting.  Play the record at 33 1/3 RPM for older clients or individuals with mental retardation.

**Novelty Dance**

Music:     Atlantic 0413113 x 45
                Alley Cat

Formation: Free formation all facing
              same direction.

| Calls | Action |
| --- | --- |
| • Right together, right together | Touch right toe to side and move back to place Repeat |
| • Left together, left together | Touch left toe to side and move back to place Repeat |
| • Right back, right back | Touch right toe to floor behind and close.  Repeat |
| • Left back, left back | Touch left toe to floor behind and close.  Repeat |
| • Right knee, right knee | Lift right knee twice |
| • Left knee, left knee | Lift left knee twice |
| • Right knee once | Lift right knee once |
| • Left knee once | Lift left knee once |
| • Clap and turn | Clap hands, and with a hopping turn, face to the right |

Repeat to end of music.  There will be two complete turns.  When facing front the last time there is only time to do each action once.

The call is:  right together, left together, right back, left back, right knee, left knee, clap and bow.

*Seated Variation*:  Use arms-right arm twice (like lifting a weight), left arm twice (same action); right arm out twice (arms at side, swing forearm out from elbow), left arm out twice (same action); right elbow (with arms at side and forearms raised to shoulder, raise arms to side), left elbow (same action); shrug right shoulder, shrug left shoulder, nod head and clap.

**Line Dance**

Virginia Reel

Music:      Windsor  4166 x 45
            Golden Reel
            (any reel type music will do)

Formation: Double line of partners
           facing each other

Note:  The actual "reeling" is not done in this version which has been adapted for use with frail elderly.  For this dance it is best to have a 1:1 volunteer ratio.  Volunteers should alternate with clients down each line.

| Call | Action |
|---|---|
| **Part 1** | |
| • Forward and bow | Everyone forward and touch partner's hands and smile |
| • Forward and change places | Change places with partner in other line |
| • Forward and change back | Pass back to own place |
| • Forward and two hands around | Join hands with partner and turn once around |
| **Part 2** | |
| • Head couples stroll down center | Head couple join hands and walk down between the lines |
| • And back again | Turn separately and return |
| **Part 3** | |
| • Cast off, ladies go right and gents go left | Everyone faces front of hall.  Head couples separate and lead others down outside of line |
| • Make an arch and others go through | At the foot, head couples meet and make an arch for other couples to go through as they meet |

Continue until all have been head couple.

*Wheelchair Variations*:  Volunteers stand behind wheelchairs (two lines, partners opposite) Same calls.  On bow, chairs brought even, right to right.  Clients shake hands and smile.  Have wheelchairs spaced so they can pass right to right when making arch on Part 3, have lead couple far enough apart to allow wheelchairs through two abreast.

## Breaks And Ending

A refreshment break about two-thirds of the way through the program is desirable. A cool drink is better than a warm one, even in the cold months. Keep the refreshments simple. There are a lot of people to serve and volunteers need a little break before going on with the dance. They shouldn't have to spend the whole break serving refreshments.

During the break, have some of the staff dance. Clients enjoy watching staff members dance a waltz or polka. It is also a good time to do some couple dancing with ambulatory or wheelchair clients. Waltzes, fox-trots, and two-steps are especially good for this part of the program.

Any successful program should end before the group gets tired of dancing. Select a quiet dance to slow things down before ending. Sometimes it is helpful to end with a quiet dance which was done earlier in the program. After officially closing the program with a goodbye to everyone, play a waltz. This is nice for the clients to listen to while they wait to be transported back to their rooms. Be sure to thank everyone for coming and have them give themselves a round of applause for a great program.

Planning and leading dances is not difficult, but it does take some practice. Once a few dances with the techniques for teaching them have been mastered, the experience becomes very fulfilling for the leader and fun for the participants.

## Resources

**Dance**

Caplow-Lindner, E., Harpaz, L. and Samberg, S. (1979). *Therapeutic Dance Movement*. New York, NY: Human Sciences Press.

Harris, J. A., Pittman, A. M. and Waller, M. S. (1978). *Dance a While*. Minneapolis, MN: Burgess Publishing Company.

Hill, K. (1976). *Dance for Physically Disabled Persons*. Washington, DC: Information and Research Utilization Center.

Lerman, L. (1984). *Teaching Dance to Senior Adults*. Springfield, IL: Charles C. Thomas.

**Records**

| | | |
|---|---|---|
| Folk Dancer Record Service | World Tone Music Company | Shirly Boyd |
| P.O. Box 2305 | 230 Seventh Avenue | 3581 Tillbury Ave |
| North Babylon, NY 11703 | New York, NY 10011 | Columbus, OH 43220 |
| Ph: 516-661-3866 | Ph: 212-691-1934 | Ph: 614-294-2473 |

# NOTES

# CHAPTER 16

# DRAMATICS, STORYTELLING AND MUSIC

**Creative Dramatics**

**Storytelling**

**Music**

**Resources**

# DRAMATICS, STORYTELLING AND MUSIC

This chapter is included for those leaders who do not feel qualified to conduct such "creative" activities as dramatics, storytelling, or music. There may even be some ideas for those who have been in the field for some time.

The following activities are not sufficient for maintaining a specialized program in any of the areas. They are presented as suggestions to be utilized to initiate drama, music and storytelling activities into the ongoing program.

## Creative Dramatics

The possibilities of using dramatics with older adults are almost endless. It is usually perceived that creative ability is limited to the young. Not so! The elderly still have that ability, although it may be buried under a great amount of reserve.

Dramatics can be employed as an activity in a variety of programs, from reminiscence to exercise. The program often begins as a four to six week interest group and ends up as a popular club activity. Dramatics offers an opportunity for creative expression which is not readily available in most recreation programs. These creative activities may be used with the slightly disoriented client, as well as with those who are mentally alert.

### Drama Session Format

A session can include 12 to 15 clients and should last 45 minutes to an hour. Following are some sample activities and a suggested format for a dramatics session.

- warm-up
  - physical imagery exercise
  - verbalization exercise

- creative activities
  - pantomime
  - verbal emotions
  - use of props
  - use of scripts
  - script development

- assignment for next session
  - plan an imaginary trip
  - bring a poem
  - answer this question

- wrap-up
  - imaginary trip
  - closing

## Warm-up Exercises

Several exercises should be used as the beginning of each session to relax the participants. These exercises fall under two categories:  physical and vocal.

## Physical Warm-up

Use one or more of these activities to help the group relax and to set the tone for the session.

- grocery shopping
  - The clients follow the leader's story as an imaginary cart is pushed through the store and "items" are lifted from the shelves and placed in their carts.

- fishing from a rowboat
  - Packing the gear, loading the boat, rowing to the spot, baiting the hook, casting the line, catching a fish and reeling it in are all possible tasks for the group.

- doing laundry the old-fashioned way
  - They fill the tub, shave soap into it, scrub the clothes on the washboard, rinse them, wring them by hand, and hang them on the line to dry.

- other suggestions
  - mow and trim the lawn
  - plant a tree
  - house cleaning

## Verbal Warm-up

These group activities encourage the group to vocalize in unison.  This helps them to feel comfortable when there is an opportunity for verbal self expression.

- emotions
  - On the count of "three," the group is to repeat the phrase given by the leader using a designated emotion.  Suggested emotions are, "happy," "sad," "angry," and "excited."

- phrases
  - "welcome everyone"
  - "you make me angry"
  - "it's raining"
  - "hi neighbor"
  - "I love you"
  - "you are special"

- getting acquainted
  - Everyone says their name the way they feel.
  - Everyone uses an adjective before their name which starts with the same letter as their name ( Happy Henry, Sad Sarah).
  - Each person says his/her name and gives the name of the person on each side.

## Pantomime

There are many activities that use actions rather than words to describe a situation. Such activities can be challenging and even provide exercise for the clients. Begin with the simple ones and progress to the more difficult challenges as the clients gain confidence in their abilities.

- creative expressions
  - facial expressions
  - laugh, sad, angry, happy, cry, smile
  - eating expressions
    banana, orange, lemon, strawberry, watermelon
  - face passing
    Create an expression and pass it to the next person who imitates it.
  - Act out simple situations such as shaving, brushing teeth, or combing hair.

- it's magic
  - magic ball
    Pass an imaginary ball around the circle. Each shows its size and does something with it before passing it on.
  - magic clay
    Each person creates an imaginary object from the magic "clay." The group tries to guess what the object is before passing the "clay" to the next person.

- mirroring
  - Two people face each other and work together. One is the "mirror" while the other makes motions to be followed. Start with one hand and remember that the mirror does it in reverse.

- toy shop
  - Each person is given a slip of paper with the name of a toy on it. Each person takes a turn to act out his/her "toy" for the others to guess. Suggestions for toys include soldier, drummer, teddy bear, truck.

*Pantomime Situations*

Make a copy of the following situations and cut them into separate slips, each bearing a single situation. Select those suitable to the abilities of the participants and hand each person a slip. Each person takes a turn at pantomiming the situation they were given and the rest of the group tries to guess it after the action is completed.

## Pantomime Situations

- Drop a ring down a sink drain and fish it out with coat hanger.

- Put on a button-up jacket that was wrong side out.

- Conduct a school band that is learning a new song.

- Brush your teeth with baking soda.

- Rake leaves into a big pile and then a strong wind blows them away.

- Picking flowers in your garden with a big bee buzzing around you.

- Chewing bubble gum—and a big bubble bursts in your face.

- Driving a stick shift car for the very first time.

- While playing golf you hit a hole-in-one.

- Climb a stepladder and change a bulb in the ceiling light fixture.

- Test the pool temperature, and then jump in the water.

- While stirring a pot of chocolate the spoon falls in.

- Try on a new pair of shoes that are too narrow.

- Batting a ball that goes through a neighbor's plate glass window.

- Drinking a cup of very hot tea and you spill some on your lap.

- Turn on the garden hose and no water comes out until you look in the end.

- Trying to find the light switch in a strange dark room.

- Rowing a boat for the very first time.

- Eat a triple-deck ice cream cone on a very hot day.

- In the shower the water turns from hot to cold and back again.

- With a large arm full of packages you try to find the key to your door.

- You run out of the bathroom in the nude to answer the phone and the drapes are open.

## Pantomime Situations
(Continued)

- Shave with a straight razor and cut yourself several times.

- Catch and land what appears to be a large fish and turns out to be an old shoe.

- You're on a ladder picking apples when the wind starts to blow you around.

- You buy a jacket at a flea market and find a $100 bill in the side pocket.

- In the middle of your tight wire act a gust of wind makes you almost fall.

- Climb on the roof to make repairs and your ladder is gone when you want to get down.

- You are an Alka-Seltzer™ tablet that has just been dropped into a glass of water.

- Brushing your long hair after riding a motorcycle and not wearing a helmet.

- While shampooing your hair the water pressure drops to a slow drizzle.

- Step outside in a light dressing gown to get the paper and are locked out.

- Try to start a campfire when all of the wood is wet.

- Fly a kite in a stiff breeze and have to tie on an extra amount of tail.

- You start to sing a solo and suddenly you lose your voice.

- Mowing the lawn you run over a nest of yellow jackets and they come after you.

- You are playing a flute in a marching band when the belt holding up your pants breaks.

- You're holding your new niece and suddenly you feel very wet.

## Creating Scripts

It is often difficult to find scripts with appropriate length and content for this population group. It is often best to create scripts using client ideas. The group will enjoy working with stories they helped to create and being involved with the development makes it easier for them to remember the story line.

Begin by using familiar activities and situations. Put together short skits based on the clients' responses to the following situations.

- Complete the statement:
  - If I had a million dollars . . .
  - Spring is . . .
  - My favorite thing is . . .
  - I'd like to go to . . .

- Using simple props:
  - Give a large bandanna to the first person in the circle. They have to do something with it before passing it to the next person who uses it for different purpose.
  - In groups of 3 or 4 persons, each one is given an object and the group makes up a story using all of the objects.
  - Put several items in a paper bag. Give the bag to a small group and have have them prepare a skit using the items as props.

## Wrapping Up the Session

This is a time to help the group relax before leaving. Give an assignment for the next session such as everyone must bring a poem to the group. Then take them on an imaginary trip. Have them close their eyes and describe the trip for them. Use as many images as possible and give them time to think about the images described. Be sure to bring them back to the facility before having them opening their eyes. Don't forget to thank them for coming—after a few sessions one of the clients might lead the trip.

# Storytelling

People of all ages like stories if they are well done. Remember, before the days of radio and television, storytelling was one of the most enjoyable forms of entertainment. Recreation leaders can become storytellers and through stories, set an example for the clients who can also become accomplished storytellers.

## Getting Started

Anyone can be a storyteller. Relating a personal interesting incident, or one that was observed, or making up something that might have happened to someone is storytelling. Getting some books from the local library that have age-suitable stories and learning to tell them is another approach.

After reading a story several times, think of the audience and the setting where it will be used. Make a mental outline of the order of events in the story, the characters, the climax and the ending. Make some notes on cards, if necessary, and practice telling the story. It is best not to try to memorize it word for word, for if a part is forgotten the teller might get lost.

When telling the story to a group, be aware of the listeners at all times. Use good eye contact and make each person feel that the story is being told to him or her alone. There are times to talk loud and times to speak softly, but make sure that everyone can hear all of the time. Vary the pace and pitch—never use a monotone. Pause before any surprises in the story to make them more effective.

Talk clearly and project your voice. Be enthusiastic! That's all there is to being a story-teller!

## Client Storytellers

Clients are great storytellers! It's just a matter of getting them started. The following ideas have proven successful with many older people. Just state a subject, give them a minute to think about it and call on the first person to start.

- the scariest thing that ever happened to you
- the most exciting adventure you ever had
- the best gift you received as a child
- the funniest thing that ever happened to you
- your first job
- your best job
- your first date
- how you met your spouse
- how your parents met
- games you played as a child
- special family holiday traditions
- weather signs and prediction sayings
- planting and harvesting by signs of the moon
- stories told by parents and grandparents
- historical events that affected your family
- superstitions or beliefs held by your parents
- oldtime crafts practiced by your family
- gatherings you attended as a child or young person

When the clients become comfortable with simple stories they will be able to participate in telling longer tales. Some of the better presentations may be grouped together and used as a part of a special event. Many of the stories could be taped and transcribed for the facility's newsletter. Most clients like to see their names and stories in print.

With a little effort, storytelling by staff and clients can become a popular activity in the recreation program.

# Music

Many recreation leaders feel that they have too little musical ability to lead activities in this area. With some enthusiastic brainstorming, even the most unmusical staff can plan activities relating to music.

## Sing-a-Longs

There are usually volunteers that can lead an occasional sing-a-long. They often bring their accompanist with them and do a great job with a fairly large group.

In between those times, use sing-a-long records with small groups. It helps them to remember the old songs and have the joy of singing them. For the clients that don't sing, but like to listen, make a tape of the old songs from records and provide a tape player with earphones for individual listening.

## Rhythm Bands

The so called "Kitchen Bands" have been around for many years. Some bands still perform for groups outside the facility. The success of such groups seems to be dependent upon having someone who is an excellent pianist available for practices and performances.

The same instruments—kazoos, sandpaper block, rhythm sticks and the like—can be used with a music interest group that is willing to play along with good Dixieland recordings.

Each member of the group should have his/her own kazoo which they bring to the sessions. Perhaps there are some harmonica players that would like to join, too. And many of the old timers remember how to play the "spoons" or the "bones."

## Band Concerts

Contact the local musician's union about having a musical group come to the agency to entertain the clients. Most of the unions will pay their members to do a specified number of benefit performances each year. Be sure to ask for a group that plays music the clients will like. A "heavy metal" group would be a little out of place for most older adults!

Larger facilities may be able to schedule a local high school or community band for a concert. Few activities will arouse more interest than an outdoor band concert on a summer evening. If the band can't come to the facility, try to take some of the clients to a concert at the park.

## Other Musical Activities

- name the tune
- musical charades, where the clients are given song titles to act out for the rest to guess.
- musical bingo. Make up bingo-like cards with the names of tunes in the squares. When the tunes are played on the stereo, the clients cover the proper square.
- silent instruments. Secure some small electronic keyboard instruments provided with earphones for musically-inclined clients to use in their rooms without disturbing others.

A staff member with little musical talent can provide a wide variety of music activities for the clients.  Additional programs such as sing-a-longs should be conducted by volunteers on a regular basis.

## Resources

Burger, I. B. (1980).  *Creative Drama for Senior Citizens*.  Wilton, CT:  Morehouse Barton Company Inc.

Gray, P. G. (1974).  *Dramatics for the Elderly*.  New York, NY:  Teachers College Press.

Greenblatt, F. S. (1985).  *Drama with the Elderly*.  Springfield, IL:  Charles C. Thomas Publishing.

Howard, V. (1978).  *Pantomimes, Charades and Skits*.  Franklin, OH:  Eldridge Publishing.

Thurman, A. H., and Piggins, C. A.  (1982).  *Drama Activities with Older Adults*.  New York, NY:  The Haworth Press.

**Storytelling**

National Storytelling Resource Center
P.O. Box 112
Jonesboro, TN  37659

# CHAPTER 17

# MAKING THINGS

**Meeting Individual Needs**

**Selecting Projects**

**Activities With Natural Materials**

**Less-Than-An-Hour Projects**

**Easy Holiday Crafts**

**Toys Of The Past**

**Let's Build A Kite**

**For The Birds**

**Making And Decorating Paper**

**Resources**

# MAKING THINGS

The task of finding challenging projects for the clients is one that takes precious time which most therapeutic recreation specialists have difficulty scheduling.  The activities and projects which appear in this section have added new dimensions to many crafts programs.

Although none of the traditional craft activities have been included, they are still found to be useful.  The authors are suggesting these additional ideas to make the present programs even more challenging.  Projects that will be suitable for male clients have been taken into consideration, as well as items which can be made for gifts or for sale at bazaars.

## Meeting Individual Needs

The following suggestions have been compiled from many sources and include techniques that should assist the clients in meeting the challenges of selecting and completing their projects.

### Helpful Techniques

- To assist those who have difficulty holding onto objects, attach flat items to the work table with masking tape, duct tape, modeling clay or floral putty.
- Use double-sided masking tape to secure jars, paint bottles or other small containers to 4 inch square pieces of cardboard to reduce spills from tipping.
- The small plastic cups from measured iced tea or lemonade mix make excellent individual glue or paint containers if glued to square cardboard bases to prevent spills.
- Fasten looms, stitchery hoops and weaving frames to the table with C-clamps to hold them steady.
- Place a small lump of modeling clay on the end of a nail or tack to hold it in place. After starting the nail or tack with a hammer, remove the clay.  This technique saves a lot of injured fingers.
- Build up the handles of tools to make it easier for clients with disabled fingers to hold brushes and crochet hooks by wrapping them with foam rubber.  Scraps are usually available at no cost from upholstery shops.
- Support the client's elbows by using foam rubber or folded towels placed on the arms of the chairs.
- Fasten a box to the side of the clients chair with clamps to hold needed tools.
- To make sandpaper easier to use, staple or tack it to a block of wood.
- Have easy-to-slip-on aprons available for messy projects.
- Thread needles by placing the yarn between a folded strip of paper which is cut to fit through the eye of the needle.
- When possible, choose water-based paints and glues.  Not only is clean-up easier, but they are better for clients with respiratory problems.
- Avoid aerosol products when clients are present for they may irritate their respiratory systems.
- Clients should use masks when sanding or doing any task where there might be dust.

*The Visually Impaired*

- Select projects where there is extreme contrast between the light and dark elements.
- Choose very simple patterns.  Patterns made of heavy cardboard or thin wood are easier to trace around.
- Read the labels concerning directions, warnings and ingredients to the clients.
- Use table or chest mounted magnifiers with plenty of nonglare lighting.

*Sensitive Skin*

- Use disposable plastic gloves.
- Avoid wool yarns and fabrics;
- Using mild hand cream before and after work often helps.

*Arthritic Hands*

- Select activities such as rug hooking, latch hooking and weaving with thick yarn.
- Use electric scissors for cutting cloth and an X-Acto® knife for cutting yarn rather than regular scissors.
- Clay and other cold or damp substances may cause stress to sensitive hands.

## Selecting Projects

Crafts should never be considered a diversionary activity, yet in many programs the projects used provide little challenge, little planning and even less consideration in meeting the needs of the client.  As an example of this the authors once visited a craft room where the clients were seated at a table, each one wrapping yarn around a coat hanger.  At the same table, in full view of the "wrappers," was another group of clients unwinding the yarn from hangers and winding it into balls!  It was obvious that this activity fell under the heading of "busywork" and was most degrading to the clients, even if they were at a fairly low functioning level.

The activities which follow are for a variety of client levels.  Leaders should try each activity before using them with clients to determine the functioning level with which it would be most effectively used.  Samples should be prepared in advance to stimulate imaginations.  New crafts should be introduced one at a time in order to make the client's choices less complicated.

## Activities With Natural Materials

The following activities may be used indoors or outside.  Whenever the weather permits, some activities should take place in the out-of doors.  Almost any level of client will enjoy these activities, if properly presented.

### Leaf Printing

Place a leaf on a sheet of paper with old newspaper underneath to protect the table.  Pour a small amount of poster paint onto a plastic plate and spread it around.  Wet a small sponge in water and squeeze it as dry as possible. Dab the sponge in the paint and then dab it up and down on the plate to get an even coating of paint on the surface of the sponge.

Holding the leaf in place, dab the sponge around the outside edge of the leaf in such a manner as to color the paper around the leaf. Carefully lift the leaf to reveal the design on the paper. This method can be used to decorate invitations, note paper, or to make decorations for a party.

### Leaf Spattering

Place a leaf on a piece of paper on a newspaper covered table. A piece of heavy corrugated cardboard under the newspaper will make the next step easier.

Use straight pins or thumb tacks to hold the leaf in place. With a small amount of poster paint on a plastic plate, dip an old toothbrush in it to coat the bristles. Hold the brush above the leaf with the bristles pointing down. Use a popsicle stick to rub across the bristles spattering the paint on the paper. Different colors of paint may be used to vary the design. When finished, remove the leaf carefully and let the paint dry. Note paper and invitations can also be decorated in this manner.

### Fruit/Vegetable Printing

Oranges, apples, carrots, lemons and potatoes all work well for this activity. Cut the fruit/ vegetable in two and dip the cut end in a small amount of poster paint which has been put in a margarine cup.

Use newsprint on a table covered with newspaper. Use the fruit/vegetable to imprint designs on the newsprint. Keep the layer of paint thin so that the design will dry quickly. When using vegetables, designs may be carved in them before dipping in the paint.

When on a picnic, tape the newsprint down to the table or geri-tray and have the clients decorate their own "tablecloth."

### Sponge Printing

Cut old sponges into a variety of natural shapes which might be found in the out-of-doors. Use them in the same way as described for vegetable prints.

## Less-Than-An-Hour Projects

There is real joy in making things from simple materials. Start with easy projects so the participants may achieve success. Select more challenging projects as follow-ups.

### Pinecone Bird Feeders

Tie a cord to the top of a large pinecone. Use a spoon to force peanut butter into the cavities of the cone. Place some birdseed on wax paper and roll the pinecone in it. Hang the feeder on a tree branch.

## Nature Critters

In the fall, collect a variety of pinecones, teasel, acorns and other nuts.  Use your imagination to make a variety of small critters.  A little glue and some patience will result in rabbits, mice, owls, and ducks.

They make nice gifts or sale items for the annual bazaar.

## Peanut Puppets

This project requires a supply of large roasted peanuts in their shells.  Also needed is white glue. yarn for hair, scrap cloth for clothing and marking pens to add facial features.

Carefully break away the bottom of the shell and remove one peanut to make room for the little finger to be inserted.  Draw a face and glue on some "hair."  Cut clothing out of scraps and glue it on.  Great gifts!

## Cartoon Pins

These pins are fun to make and give to a child to wear.  Choose a character from the Sunday paper that is easy to cut out.  Cut the panel in which the character appears from the paper and use white glue to cement it to a piece of thin cardboard, such as tablet back.  After the glue has dried use scissors to cut around the figure.

Use tape to fasten a small safety pin to the back, making sure that the figure hangs correctly.  Lay the pin on wax paper, face up.  Using a cotton swab, coat the front of the pin with white glue (it will dry clear).  Give it several more coats letting it dry between them.  That's all there is to it!

## Cricket Cage

Two opaque bases from one-liter plastic bottles can be used to make a cage.  A piece of 6" x 12" plastic screen should be rolled into a cylinder and stapled to fit snugly inside one of the bases.  The other base serves as the cap.  Catch a cricket and place it in the cage with a little grass.  Make sure to keep it in the shade.

In the late summer crickets start to "sing."  Listen for them, and catch one that sings, for the cage.  This is important since only male crickets make the sound by rubbing their hind leg against a wing.  Keep him caged for no more than a day or two before releasing him.  The rate at which the cricket makes the sound is related to the temperature.  If you count the number of "chirps" in a 15 second period and add 40, the result will be within two or three degrees of the temperature.

A very simple cage can be made by placing a cricket in a plastic cup with a few leaves in it and covering it with nylon net held in place with a rubber band.

## Making a Terrarium

Use a two-liter clear plastic soft drink bottle and remove the opaque base. Cut the bottle off about six inches from the bottom. Naptha fuel may be used to a remove the label. This should be done by a staff member in a well-ventilated area. Plant small plants or seeds in potting soil in a margarine container placed in the opaque bottle bottom. Invert the clear plastic bottle-part with the dome up and insert it in the opaque bottom. Now put it on a window sill and enjoy the miniature terrarium.

## Tissue-Covered Greeting Cards

Interesting greeting cards may be made by covering small leaves or ferns with cleansing tissue. The process is simple and easy to learn. Be sure to master it yourself before trying to teach it to others.

Use a 5" x 8" piece of paper folded to be a 4" x 5" card. Place a small piece of fern or a pressed flower in the desired position on the front of the card.

Place the folded card, with the front side up, on a sheet of wax paper before the next step. Now place a single thickness of cleansing tissue over the entire card front.

Use a foam rubber brush to dab white glue, which has been thinned (one part water, two parts glue) over the surface of the tissue. Be careful not to tear the tissue.

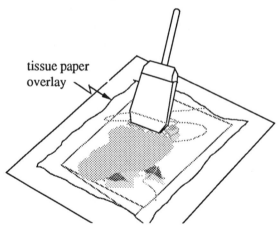

tissue paper overlay

After the glue has dried, trim the tissue even with the face of the card.

The card is now ready for any message desired.

## Découpage

Decorate a box, or make a montage on heavy cardboard using this procedure. Have a supply of magazines for pictures, cardboard boxes, and sheets of cardboard on hand before beginning. Prepare the white glue by thinning it one-third with water (one part water, two parts glue). Foam rubber brushes work well for applying the glue and are easily cleaned with water.

Cut out pictures and arrange them to cover the board or box. Coat the surface of the board or box with the prepared glue. Use water and sponge to dampen the back of the pictures and arrange them on the glue covered surface, face up. Smooth them down with a damp sponge working out any bubbles.

Let the work dry for an hour or more, then coat the entire surface with the glue mixture. Use two or three coats, letting the glue dry thoroughly between coats. After three coats the box or picture should shine.

Pictures mounted with this technique can be easily framed with 1/2 inch cloth tape. A picture hanger mounted on the back of the work will complete the project.

When covering boxes, make sure that the lid fits loosely so that it will not bind when the extra thicknesses of materials are applied.

## Sun Catchers

Sun catchers are easily made using clear contact paper and a variety of translucent materials, natural or man-made. Keep the size fairly small, not over 3" x 4", so that they will not curl up when hung in the window.

To start, select a small leaf or flower to be sandwiched between two pieces of contact paper. Bits of yarn, string, or colored tissue paper may be used in place of natural materials.

Cut two pieces of contact paper a little larger than the desired size. Peel the backing from one of the pieces and lay it on a smooth flat surface, sticky side up. Arrange the items on the sticky surface, being careful to keep them at least one-half inch from the edges.

Peel the backing paper from the second piece, sticky side to sticky side. Using our fingers and working from the center out, press the two pieces together to eliminate bubbles. If bubbles persist, stick a pin through them and force the air out.

Finally, using scissors or a paper cutter, trim the edges so that no sticky parts show. Use a paper punch to make a hole at the top so that a string may be inserted with which to hang the sun catcher.

Book marks can be made in the same manner. Just start with 2" x 6" pieces of contact paper.

## Rope Quoits

Quoits are rope rings used for a variety of tossing games, quoit golf being the main one. Directions for this game are found in the chapter, Activities That Promote Exercise (page 118).

Quoits 3 1/2 inches in diameter will fit in a one pound coffee can for storage. They should be made from 3/8 inch 3 strand laid rope. Polypropylene rope is best because it is fairly stiff. Do not use nylon or any type of braided rope.

Three feet of rope will make three quoits. Unwind the 3 foot piece into three separate strands. Wrap masking tape around both ends of each strand to prevent raveling while making the quoit.

To start a quoit make a 3 1/2 inch loop in the middle of the strand. Facing the loop held vertically, with the crossed ends up, make certain that the end going to the left is in front (Step 1). Hold the loop at the point where the strand crosses in the left hand and use the right hand to grasp the strand going to the right about one inch from the left hand (Step 2). Twist the strand clockwise with the right hand to keep it tight, bring it around the loop and lay it in the groove remaining from when the rope was untwisted.

The two parts of the strand are held in place by moving the left hand to the point where the part of the strand was laid into the loop.

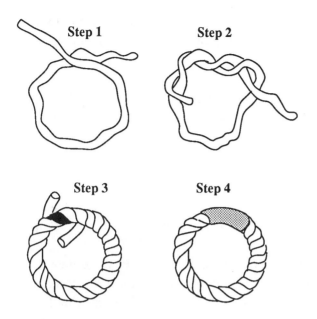

Step 1    Step 2

Step 3    Step 4

Continue this procedure until the right end of the strand is woven into place around the loop. If done correctly, the loop will begin to look like an endless rope with one strand missing.

Turn the quoit around so that the end of the strand that has not been used is extending to the right. Hold the loop in the left hand and continue twisting the new end of the strand clockwise with the right hand. Laying it in the groove in the loop as was done previously.

When the strand is laid in properly all the way around the quoit, the two short ends will be next to each other (Step 3). Cut off the excess and use colored tape to hold the ends in the groove.

The colored tape not only holds the ends secure, but by using different colors of tape, identifies the quoits for individual use (Step 4).

## Easy Holiday Crafts

### Pinecone Elves

Cut a 1 1/2 inch circle of cardboard for the base. Glue a 2 inch pinecone to the base using white glue or a glue gun. Two kidney beans should now be glued to the base for shoes. Push them under the cone far enough to look realistic. Glue an acorn onto the top of the cone which has been flattened to receive it. Make the arms from pipe cleaners and use cotton or tufts of cotton to make the hair. Draw the facial features with a small marking pen and use the acorn cap for a hat. With a little imagination, a variety of figures can be made in this manner.

### Pinecone Trees

Cut a circular cardboard base a little larger than the cone to be used for the tree. Glue the cone to the base in an upright position. Paint white glue on the tips of the petals. Sprinkle glitter or plastic snow on the glue and shake of the excess after it dries. Use small star stickers and plastic beads as tree ornaments. These small trees make great gifts or bazaar sales items.

## Burlap Wreaths

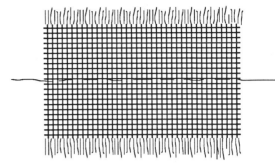

Open a wire coat hanger and cut off the hook and twisted parts then straighten the remaining wire. Cut one yard of 45 inch green or cream colored burlap into 4 and 6 inch strips. Pull out the threads to fray 1 inch on each side of the narrow strips and 2 inches on each side of the wider strips.

Weave the wire down through the center of the strips at 1/2 inch intervals. By placing a 4 inch strip on top of a 6 inch strip and weaving them together a fuller wreath can be made.

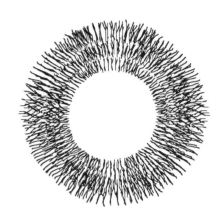

When the material is all on the wire, overlap the ends of the wire about 1 inch and secure with cloth tape. The wreath can be decorated with pine cones and ornaments to complete the decoration.

A candle ring for a large candle may be made in the same manner using finer wire and 4 inch strips of burlap.

Both of these items are fun to make and sell well at a bazaar.

## Toys Of The Past

### Buzz Saw

Large two hole buttons, 2 inches in diameter, and heavy string are needed to make this toy from the 1800s. Circles of plastic or cardboard may be used also.

The string should be about 3 feet long. Make holes in the "saw" as shown, thread the twine through and knot it securely. Hook the loops over the index fingers of each hand so that the button is suspended in the middle. Stretch the string until the button sags about 1/2 inch below the level of the fingers. Rotate the hands in a circular motion to "wind" the string. To operate, alternately pull and relax the string to make the "saw" rotate and create a buzzing sound.

### Eskimo Yo-Yo

These toys are much easier to make than to operate. Heavy wooden beads are used as weights. Acorns work but must have holes drilled in them. Tie equal weights to each end of a 30 inch piece of string. A straightened paper clip is useful in threading the string through the hole. Let the two weights hang down so that one is about 2 inches below the other and tie an overhand knot in the double string to hold the position.

To operate, hold the string at the knot in the right hand. Hold the shorter weight in the left hand. Using wrist action, start the weighted string rotating clockwise like an airplane propeller. When the weight is swinging, maintain the action by moving the right hand in an up-and-down motion. Now throw the second weight down as the first is starting on the up swing. With practice and patience it is possible to keep the weights rotating in opposite directions.

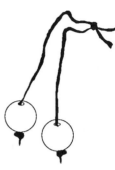

### Hummer

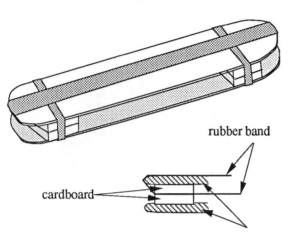

rubber band

cardboard

tongue depressors

Two 4 inch pieces of tongue depressors, three rubber bands and 4 pieces of cardboard are needed for this project. Stretch a flat rubber band lengthwise over a stick and use the cardboard to keep it from touching one side. Make a sandwich using the other two spacers. Use two small rubberbands to hold it all together. Blow through the tongue depressor sandwich.

### Whimmey Diddle

Other names for this toy include Gee-Haw stick, kazoo-kaza, and Yip stick. It is operated by rubbing a stick over the notches in such a manner as to control the direction of the propeller's rotation.

The handle can be a 3/8 inch square by 8 inch long piece of soft wood, or it can be a twig of about the same size. The spacing of the notches is not critical—about 3/8 inch apart and 1/4 inch deep. They can be made with a knife, or coarse sandpaper on a block of wood.

The propeller is made from a 1 1/4 inch length of popsicle stick. Make diagonal marks from the corners to find the center and drill a 1/16 inch hole. Use a 3/4 inch 19 or 20 gauge nail (not a brad) to attach the propeller, making certain that it turns freely.

To hold the whimmey-diddle, grasp the handle behind the notches holding it horizontally. Hold the rubbing stick so that the thumb touches the side of the handle as the stick is rubbed over the notches. To reverse, continue to rub over the notches, but let the edge of the index finger rub the opposite edge of the handle.

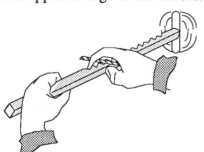

Say "kazoo" when it goes one way and "kaza" when it reverses.

### Helicopter

Find the center of a tongue depressor and drill a 3/16 inch hole.  Wet the tongue depressor in warn water and gently twist the ends in opposite directions to give it the shape of a propeller.  Use a hairdryer to dry the wood so that it will hold its new shape.  Insert an 8" x 3/16" dowel in the hole and apply a dab of fast-drying glue to the end.  Make sure that the stick is perpendicular to the propeller.

Hold the stick between the palms and rub them past each other and release the stick.  If it doesn't go up, reverse the direction that the hands are rubbed.

## Let's Build A Kite

### Sled Kite

This is one of the easiest kites to build and fly.  You will need a 13 gallon garbage bag, two 3/16" x 28 1/2" dowels and some one inch clear plastic tape.

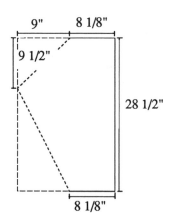

1. Lay out the pattern on wrapping paper and cut out.
2. Tape the pattern to a plastic garbage bag and cut it out.
3. Lay the kite out flat and tape dowels in place as shown.
4. Reinforce corners and use a paper punch to make holes for the bridle.
5. Cut 85 inch bridle string and tie ends through holes in the sail.
6. Find center of bridle and tie an overhand knot.
7. Tie flying line to this loop.
8. Decorate kite with permanent magic markers.

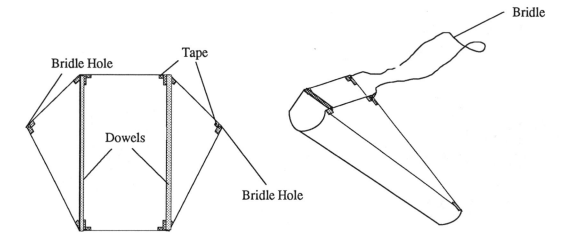

## Fish Kites

These popular kites are made from plastic or light weight paper. They are meant to be hung from the string of another kite like the sled kite.

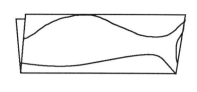

1. Cut paper or plastic 20" x 30" and fold in half lengthwise.
2. Draw the outline of the fish and cut out.
3. Tape or glue the edges together leaving ends open.
4. Draw on fish features with permanent markers.
5. Cut center out of plastic top from large coffee can to make a ring.
6. Insert ring in the mouth and tape in place.
7. Add the bridle and it's ready to hang on the string of the sled kite.

# For The Birds

Simple construction projects can give a great deal of satisfaction. These projects are particularly well suited to male clients, but many of the women might like to make them also. The materials can usually be obtained from the "shorts" box at the local lumber yard at very little cost.

If tools are not available, or if clients can not operate them, check with a local high school shop teacher to see if the parts might be mass-produced by the students.

## Bird houses

Make sure that the houses are designed for birds that frequent the area where they are to be placed. Follow the directions carefully for hole size in order to attract the desired species.

Wrens and chickadees are attracted by houses that are approximately 4" x 4" x 7". The hole should be 1 inch in diameter and 6 inches above the ground.

Phoebes and robins are attracted to open boxes. The base should be about 7" x 7" with the roof 9 inches from the bottom. Place the boxes 10 feet above the ground.

All of the houses should have 1/4 inch ventilation holes in the bottom. Stain them a woodsy color or let them weather naturally.

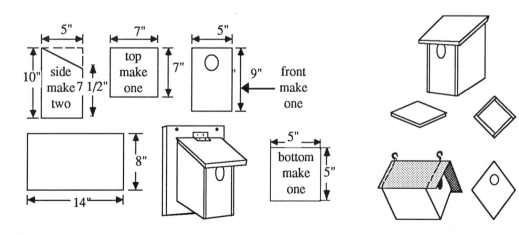

Experiment with different materials and designs.  Roof shingles, plastic bottles, and pieces of bark all have possibilities.

They may be put up around the grounds, or constructed as sale items for a bazaar.

## Bird Feeders

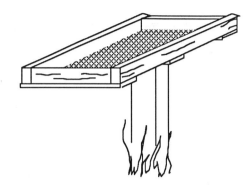

To attract birds in the winter, install feeders.  Commercial feeders are expensive, but simple ones may be constructed by the clients at a fraction of the cost.

The open feeder is the easiest to construct.  The measurements can vary depending on the scrap wood available.  The bottom is a piece of plastic screen to let water drain through.

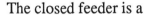

The closed feeder is a little more complicated and should be constructed by those clients with higher skill levels.  Again, there are no specific measurements. It all depends on what is available.  Parts for this feeder could be cut out by a volunteer with a home workshop, if the clients do not have access to tools.  After the parts are cut out, the only tool necessary is a hammer.

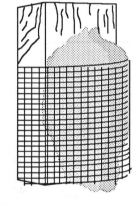

The suet board is a good project for any one with minimal skills.  The suet compartment is usually enclosed with 1/2 inch mesh hardware cloth, the material from a plastic mesh vegetable bag will also work.

Install the feeders close to a large window where they can be easily seen.  If there are trees or shrubs nearby the birds will soon visit.  Watching the colorful birds will provide hours of enjoyment for all of the clients.

# Making And Decorating Paper

## Paper Making

The first real paper was made by wasps. The Chinese discovered the process about 105 AD. A thousand years later the process was brought to Europe. Paper can be made from wood fibers, grass, weeds, corn husks, or cloth. Try easy ones first, like grass or cornhusks. A blender or food processor may be used to chop the fibers very fine.

Step 1.
Make two frames the same size out of 1/2 inch square wood. Any size that fits into a square plastic dishpan is good. A 5" x 8" size would be right for a greeting card. Staple a piece of window screen to one frame which is called the mold. The plain frame is called the deckle.

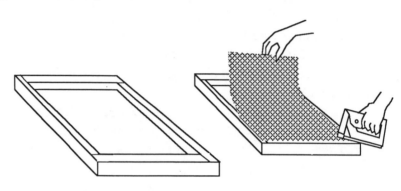

Step 2.
Cut vegetable fibers as fine as possible until there are enough to fill a 10 quart plastic pail half full. Cover with warm water and add two tablespoons (estimate) of lye and let set overnight, or longer. This will help separate the fibers.

Step 3.
Put soaked fibers in a blender, a small amount at a time, add water and chop as fine as possible. Add bits of finely torn newsprint or paper towel (A couple of paper towels should do it). Strain this slurry into a square plastic dishpan using a colander. Add warm water until the pan is almost full. The consistancy should be that of whole milk

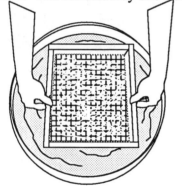

Step 4.
Hold the mold, screen side up and place the empty frame (deckle) on top. The purpose of deckle is to let the slurry drain slowly through the mold, thus forming the "wet leaf." Hold the two parts together and dip them vertically into the slurry. Stir the mixture just before you dip to keep the fibers in suspension.

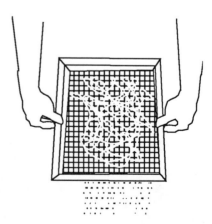

Step 5.
Turn the deckle and mold to a horizontal position and lift it out of the slurry. Shake the frames slowly as the slurry drains through the screen to set the fibers. The wet leaf is now on the screen.

Step 6.

Set the frames down on several thicknesses of newspaper and remove the deckle. Place several pieces of clean newsprint on top of the wet leaf and turn the frame and "blotter" paper face down on the table.

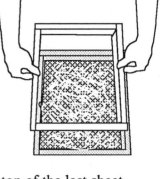

Step 7.

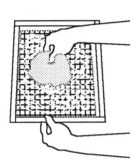

Sponge excess water away through the screen and carefully lift the mold, leaving the wet leaf on the blotter. Put another blotter on top of the wet leaf and keep stacking the wet leaves of paper in this manner as you make them. Place several pieces of newspaper under the pile and on top of the last sheet. Use a board with a heavy weight like a concrete block on top of the stack to force out the excess water.

Step 8.

When most of the water has been forced out, remove the sheets of new paper and press them dry with a warm iron. Press the blotter paper dry and reuse it.

Step 9.

Congratulate yourself for you've just made paper! Now try other plant fibers and see how many different kinds of paper you can make.

## Silkscreening

Simple silkscreen techniques can be utilized by all but those with the lowest skill levels to produce note and greeting cards. Water soluble silkscreen ink, and rubber squeegee, and silk screen grade organdy can be purchased from most art supply stores. The 11" x 14" frame can be made, or an artist's canvas frame can be purchased. Other materials include masking tape, writing paper for the design, and paper on which to print.

Step 1. The Frame

Stretch and staple the organdy to the frame, using an ordinary paper stapler. Cover the staples with masking tape. Use a couple of two inch loose-pin hinges to fasten the frame to a 12" x 15" plywood base. The pins may be pulled and the frame removed for cleaning. Use tape to mask the inside of the frame and screen so that when the paper is placed underneath, there will be a 1/2 inch border on the print.

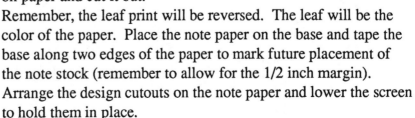

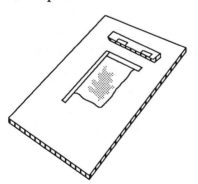

Step 2. The Design

Select a design such as leaves or a flower, trace it on paper and cut it out.

Remember, the leaf print will be reversed. The leaf will be the color of the paper. Place the note paper on the base and tape the base along two edges of the paper to mark future placement of the note stock (remember to allow for the 1/2 inch margin). Arrange the design cutouts on the note paper and lower the screen to hold them in place.

Step 3. The Printing
Put a layer of ink about 1/4 inch thick by 1/2 inch wide across the screen above the design. Hold the frame down tightly and use the squeegee to wipe the ink across the screen. Ink will be forced through the screen on to the paper. It will also adhere the design to the screen for future prints.

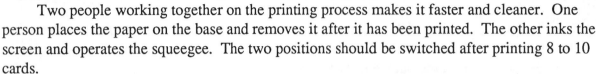

*Helpful Hints*
The leader should work through the process enough times to become thoroughly familiar with it before using it as a craft with a group.

Two people working together on the printing process makes it faster and cleaner. One person places the paper on the base and removes it after it has been printed. The other inks the screen and operates the squeegee. The two positions should be switched after printing 8 to 10 cards.

After the desired number of prints have been made, the cutout can be removed and the next design can be adhered in the same manner unless a different colored ink is needed. Then the screen must be washed and dried before continuing.

Silkscreen ink is less expensive in 1/2 pound quantities. It dries out quickly if left open. Transferring to large mouth baby food jars makes it easier to handle and prevents it from drying out as quickly. Be sure to cap the ink tightly when not in use.

A tongue depressor is useful for transferring ink to the screen and for scraping ink build-up from the squeegee. Be careful not to add too much ink to the screen at a time.

Be sure to clean the screen immediately after use. If the ink dries, the screen will become unusable and have to be replaced. If a sink with a spray hose is available, clean up is simplified. If not, use a small vegetable brush under a faucet.

The masking tape should never be left on the screen more than a few days. For easier cleanup, remove the tape before washing the screen.

Experiment with a variety of designs and techniques. This is the easiest method, and once it has been mastered other methods for making the design may be used to achieve greater detail in the finished print.

## Stenciling

Stenciling is an easy project for older adults. The technique is simple and the results quite attractive. One precaution; older adults tend to use too much paint. This leads to paint seeping under the stencil. It is best to utilize sponge or bristle brushes which have been designed for stenciling. Tempera, water colors or poster paint may be utilized, but acrylic stencil paints are available. Stencil paint is a little thicker than other types of paint making it easier to use with older adults. Stencils may be made from paper, or purchased in brass, plastic or specialized paper. Brass stencils are generally small and intricate designs. It also takes hand pressure to hold the stencil down so paint will not seep underneath. Plastic stencils are available and clean up is easy in soapy water. They are probably the best when working with clients.

Stenciling can be done on paper, wood, slate, and fabric. Start clients out with inexpensive newsprint or similar paper. Construction paper is too absorbent so it should be avoided. When working with fabric, remember it too is absorbent; therefore, less paint will be need.

Begin by putting a small amount of paint onto a paper plate. Lightly dab the top of the brush into the paint. Dab the brush onto the edge of the paper plate or a paper towel. When the brush appears dry, it is ready to stencil.

Place the stencil over a piece of paper. If the design is to be completed in more than one color, use masking tape to the portions that are not to be stenciled. Either tap (stippling) or roll the brush in a slight circular motion over the area to be stenciled. Older adults find it difficult to stipple and will try brushing over the stencil unless reminded to go in small circles.

The paint will dry quickly and the stencil can be moved to complete the other colors. A clean brush should be used with each new color. The brushes may be washed between colors, but make sure they are dry before proceeding.

Stencils and stencil supplies can be purchased at most craft shops and, with care, will be useable for several years. Craft shops usually sell books with stencil techniques and designs.

## Resources

Allison, L. (1981). *Trash Artists Workshop.* Belmont, CA: Pitman Learning Inc.

Anderson, E. (1982). *Crafts and the Disabled.* North Pomfret, VT: Batsford Publishing.

Dean, L. and Scarlett, A. (1975). *Critters, Angels and Stars.* Chadds Ford, PA: Brandywine River Museum.

Duvall, C. (1972). *Wanna Make Something Out of It?* Los Angeles, CA: Nash Publishing.

Eckstein, A. A. (1972). *How to Make Treasures from Trash.* Great Neck, NY: Hearthside Press Inc.

Fiaotto, P. (1975). *Snips and Snails and Walnut Whales.* New York, NY: Workman Publishing.

Gould, E. and Gould, L. (1978). *Arts and Crafts for Physically and Mentally Disabled.* Springfield, IL: Charles C. Thomas.

Grimm, G. (1968). *An Introduction to Basic Crafts.* Minneapolis, MN: Burgess Publishing.

Kirkman, W. (1981). *Nature Crafts Workshop.* Belmont, CA: Pitman Learning Inc.

van der Smissen, B. and Goering, O. H. (1977). *Nature-Oriented Activities.* Ames, IA: Iowa State University Press.

Wilson, J. L. and Misselhorn, T. M. (1991). *Easy to Do and Inexpensive Too: Crafts, Games, Homemade Game Equipment, Music, Nature and Sensory experiences.* Minneapolis, MN: Burgess Publishing Co

# NOTES

# Chapter 18

# HOMEMADE GAMES

Parlor Game Carnival

Making And Playing The Games

Collecting The Set Of Games

# HOMEMADE GAMES

Homemade games are easy to make and fun to use. Most of those described in the following pages are adapted from parlor games which were used as family entertainment before the days of commercialized recreation.

These games can be used on a 1 : 1 basis or may be played in small groups. Using 15 to 20 of the games in a large room makes a special event program much like a carnival.

The directions for playing and scoring each game should be printed in large letters on 5" x 7" cards, one card for each game. These cards are placed with the games when they are played. The suggested wording for these cards accompanies the description of how to make the game.

## Parlor Game Carnival

Place the games around the room allowing enough space for 3 or 4 people to be at each game. There should be several more games than there are groups of people playing. Post the directions for playing and scoring with each game. A number on a 3" x 5" card is posted by each game so that "teams" can keep score without having to play the games in order. Each team member has a 3" x 5" score card which has the numbers of all of the games on it.

The group moves to a game and each person plays it, in turn, and records the score on his/her card next to the number of the game. After everyone in the group has played the game, the group moves to another, until all games have been played (or the time for the party is up).

At the end of the party, individual scores are totaled and simple prizes awarded. The games can be packed easily in a large box to be used another time.

## Making And Playing The Games

The suggested materials and dimensions may be changed to meet the needs of the agency. The same holds for the directions and scoring. The ideas presented here have been workable in a number of residential facilities.

When collecting the materials to make the games, consider the problems of storage and sturdiness. The authors' complete set fits in a 3' x 3' x 3' cardboard box and has been in use more than ten years.

### Egg Toss

Equipment: five table tennis balls and a three-dozen egg separator from the dietary department. Use Avery labels to designate a score of 5, 10, 15, 20 for each compartment.

Game: Place the egg separator on a table. Placing the table against a wall will save chasing the balls that miss their target.

Directions: From a distance of two feet, bounce each ball on the table trying to make it land in the highest scoring compartment possible. After all five balls have been tossed, add the scores from each compartment in which a ball lands.

## Clothespin Drop

Equipment: Five regular wooden clothespins and a one gallon wide-mouth plastic jar.

Game:  Place the jar under the edge of a table so that a player can sit in a chair and rest a forearm on the edge of the table.  Release the clothespins one at a time so that they will fall into the jar.  To make the game more difficult use a plastic lid on the jar with a 3 inch circular hole that the pins must go through to land in the jar, or use a jar with a smaller opening.

Directions:  Sit in the chair and rest a forearm on the edge of the table.  Hold a clothespin by the end and drop it into the jar. Repeat until all clothespins have been dropped.  Score 20 points for each clothspin  that remains in the jar.

(Chair and jar may be reversed at the table if the player wishes to use the other hand).

## Snap Shot

Equipment:  Five checkers and a 12" x 24" piece of cardboard laid out as shown with a 6 inch square.

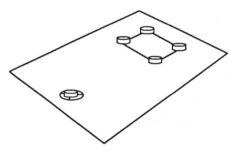

Game:  Place the gameboard on a table. Players may stand or sit.  Place a checker on each corner of the square and one on the "X."

Directions:  Place the third finger on the thumb of that hand and, holding the thumb next to the checker on the "X," snap the checker trying to make it land inside the square.  Five trials.  Score 20 points each  time the checker is snapped and comes to rest completely inside the square without disturbing the corner checkers.

## Hang It

Equipment:  Five jar rubbers (found in canning supply section of grocery stores), one 16" x 24" (approximate size) piece of 1/4 inch plywood and nine "L" shaped cup hooks.  Screw cup hooks into board as shown in the diagram and label them "10, 15, 20, 25" as shown.

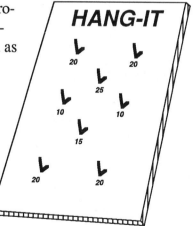

Game:  Set the board on a table against the wall with the bottom of the board about six inches from the wall.

Directions:  From a distance of three feet, toss each of the five jar rubbers at the board trying to have them hang on the highest score possible. After all have been tossed add the score of those remaining on the hooks.

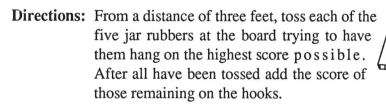

**Box Bounce**

Equipment: Small cardboard box and five tennis or rubber balls (tennis balls can usually be obtained at no charge from a tennis club which has a supply of "dead" balls).

Game: Place the box against a wall and a chair four feet in front of it. This distance may be varied depending upon the skill of the group, but should remain constant if the activity is used as part of a carnival.

> **Directions:** From a seated position toss a ball so that it bounces on the floor before landing in the box. Five trials. Score 20 points for each ball that remains in the box after all five balls have been thrown.

**Roll-a-Bowl**

Equipment: A cardboard box approximately 12" square x 6" high, a piece of 1/8 inch hardboard or cardboard for a ramp. Five tennis or small rubber balls.

Game: Tape the ramp to the edge of the box as shown and place it on the floor against the wall. The object is to roll the balls up the ramp and have them fall in the box.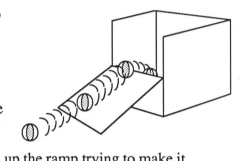

> **Directions:** From a distance of 5 feet roll each ball up the ramp trying to make it fall into the box. After all five balls have been rolled score 20 points for each ball remaining in the box.

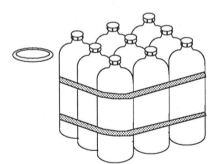

**Three-in-a-Row**

Equipment: Nine one-liter plastic soft drink bottles, five plastic one-pound coffee can lids, masking tape.

Game: Tape the nine bottles together as shown. Cut the flat inner circles from the plastic lids and use the rings thus formed. Place the cans on a chair or box in such a way that players can reach no closer than two feet from them.

> **Directions:** From a distance of two feet toss each of the five rings, trying to have them land around the neck of the bottles. Score 20 points for each successful try. Double the score if any three rings are in a row as in tic-tac-toe.

## Spot

Equipment: A piece of plywood or cardboard about 18 inches square and a flat 6 inch suction type sink stopper (a heavy plastic 6 inch plastic lid may be used instead).

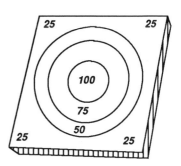

Game: Draw three concentric circles on the board having diameters of 8, 12 and 16 inches as shown in the diagram. Label the inner circle "100," the next "75" and the last "50." In each corner place a "25" as shown. Place the board on the floor to play.

> **Directions:** From a distance of five feet toss the disc onto the board. The score for the toss is determined by the largest circle (smallest number) touched by the disc. Each player tosses three times, then add the scores.

## Cup and Ball

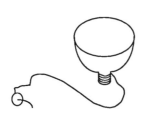

Equipment: Two liter plastic soft drink bottle, a 2 foot piece of string and a 2 inch sponge rubber ball.

Game: Cut the top of the bottle off about two inches down from the neck as shown and discard the bottom part of the bottle. Use an awl to force a hole in the ball and a large needle to pull the end of the string through. A regular knot will let the string out in a short time, so tie a heavy rubber band to the end of the string and pull it back inside the ball cutting off the excess rubber band remaining outside the ball.

tie rubber band to string and pull into ball

Tie the other end of the string to the neck of the bottle so that there is about 18 inches of string between the ball and bottle as shown in the sketch.

> **Directions:** Hold the cup by the small end with the ball dangling. Swing the cup so that the ball comes up in the air and try to catch it in the cup. Three trials with 25 points for each success.

## Muffin Tin Polo

Equipment: A six compartment cupcake pan and five 1" x 1" x 1" wooden blocks. Have someone use a table saw to make the blocks from scrap wood. Sand them smooth, give them a coat of clear finish, and use a permanent magic marker to place a value on the six sides of each block as follows—5, 10, 15, 20, 25, and 50.

Game: Place the cupcake pan on the floor against a wall. Have participants sit in a chair so that they will have to toss the blocks from a distance of three feet.

> **Directions:** From a distance of three feet toss each of the five blocks into the cupcake pan. Add up the scores that show on the tops of each block that comes to rest in the bottom of a compartment.

**Shoot a Basket**

Equipment:  A small round waste basket and a 3 or 4 inch soft rubber ball.

Game:  Place the basket on a table against the wall.  Set a chair in such a position that the participant will be shooting from a seated position about five feet away from the basket.

> **Directions:**  From a seated distance of five feet toss the ball into the basket.  Score 25 points for each time the ball lands in the basket.  Three trials.

**Croquet Golf**

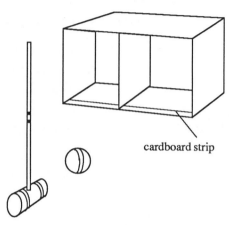

cardboard strip

Equipment:  A croquet mallet, three croquet balls and a cardboard box approximately 12" x 18" in size.  Cut the top from the box and tape a 1 inch strip of cardboard to the inside edge of one of the long sides as shown to help keep the balls in the box.

Game:  Lay the box on its side against a wall and line the balls up beside each other at a distance of eight feet from the box.  The mallet may be used from a standing or seated position to hit the balls.

> **Directions:**  From a distance of eight feet use the mallet to hit the balls into the box.  Score 25 points for each ball that remains in the box.

## Collecting The Set Of Games

Usually the entire set of games is not constructed at the same time.  Make a game, use it with the clients, and add it to the collection.  After several months, the set will be complete and there will be enough games to schedule a parlor game carnival.

# GROWING  THINGS

# GROWING THINGS

The joy of a fresh cut flower, the smell of newly turned soil, the rich feel of the earth and the sense of achievement from watching a bloom open are all reasons to involve clients in activities with growing things.

Growing activities include both gardening in the out-of-doors using garden plots or containers, and caring for plants indoors. These activities also include flower arranging, drying natural materials, working with herbs and making items with natural materials.

These activities can take place outdoors or inside all year long. They offer a great opportunity for clients to experience a sense of achievement and responsibility. In an institutionalized setting, clients often have little they *must* do during the day. Taking care of a small garden plot or house plant encourages a client to be responsible and gives him/her a sense of accomplishment.

Even if the staff is not experienced in horticultural activities, the program can still be extremely successful. Clients are an amazing wealth of information and can assist the staff. Even confused and disoriented clients often remember the joy of working with flowers and plants and will do quite well when given the opportunity. Another source of information is the local garden center. The personnel are usually extremely helpful and may be willing to offer assistance or a discount on materials and supplies.

Ideas for the growing program, along with tips for offering the program and a month by month calendar are included in this section.

## Gardening Outdoors

Many clients planted large gardens when they were younger. They remember very large gardens and are often fearful of taking on such a large project. Creating small 4' by 5' garden plots will alleviate their fears and make it easier for them to enjoy a gardening experience. Plots are small enough so that clients can reach across their entire garden easily with garden tool, yet large enough to feel like they have their own garden.

There is a sense of ownership with these small plots. This can be reinforced by putting a wooden sign in front of each plot with the gardener's name on it. It is amazing how much care the plot will receive when a person's name is on it. Care should be taken when selecting plants for the garden plots. Vining plants such as zucchini or pumpkins take a lot of room and would soon overrun the other plants. There needs to be a fair amount of corn planted side by side before pollination can take place. Therefore, a community plot is needed to grow corn and plants which vine. Although community plots are necessary for some plants, they do not foster the same sense of client responsibility, ownership and achievement as with individual garden plots.

Clients should be involved with the planning and laying out of the garden plots. They will often say that they are not capable of doing the bending and stretching involved with gardening. Four by five feet garden plots are ideal because they are small enough that even a person in a wheelchair can use garden tools to reach across the plot. Participation in the planning process can be encouraged by utilizing the tubes used to hold golf clubs in a golf bag. The plastic tubes are large enough so that seeds can be dropped down them into the soil without the client having to bend over. They work well with wheelchair clients, also.

# Container Gardening

Container gardening outdoors offers many opportunities for veteran and novice gardeners. Container gardening eliminates the need for extensive space and weeding. And, the containers can be moved around easily to receive the best lighting.

## Containers

The right container is important for successful container gardening. The container should be large enough to accommodate the plants in their mature state. The general rule is 8 to 10 inches in depth. The container should have holes for drainage so excess water can be drained easily. Water sitting in the bottom of the container will cause the roots to rot so care should be taken to ensure proper drainage. The best type of soil for container gardening is obtained at a garden center. Professionals call the mixture a "soiless mix." It has been designed specifically for container gardening.

Annuals are the most common form of container gardening, but it is possible to grow herbs and vegetables in containers.

## Annuals

It is easy to find annuals for container gardening. Select any type of container with drainage for the excess water. Barrels or old buckets make nice containers and may be easily obtained. Marigolds, zinnias, violas, pansies, portulaca, dahlias, tulips, mums, fuchsias, petunias, geraniums, alyssum, snap dragons, touch-me-nots, and periwinkle are a few of the possibilities. Check the water and lighting conditions of flowers which are to be planted together to ensure compatibility.

## Vegetables

Leafy vegetables such as lettuce, radishes, onions and herbs do well in containers. Smaller varieties of tomatoes and peppers also work well. Vining plants, such as tomatoes or cucumbers, should have their own containers. Specifications for various vegetables follow on page 175.

# Gardening Indoors

Flowers blooming on the window sill are a pleasant memory for many clients. The year-round programming possibilities make indoor gardening a worthwhile endeavor.

## Houseplants

Many beautiful houseplants can be grown by the clients indoors. Even flowering plants can be grown in the clients' rooms. A schedule of watering and fertilizing should be established with the client so the plant does not receive too much care. Some of the best plants for the clients are spider, snake, philodendron, and wandering jew. For a client who likes to water, a plant such as the heartier baby's breath or a vining fig might work well because these plants thrive in very moist soil. Since most clients like the room very warm which leads to dry conditions, plants such as ferns which need high humidity will not do well.

## Check for Problems

All plants should be checked on a regular basis for bugs and diseases. Spider mites, insects that plague houseplants, thrive in dry environments. An infested plant has dull green dropping leaves, small spider webs all over the plant, and a dusty appearance. A wash in dish detergent suds is the cure for a slight infection and malathon spray is best for a severe infestation. If chemicals are to be used remove the plant from the client's room before spraying. All sick houseplants should be kept in isolation away from healthier houseplants. There are many books available at the library, bookstore or garden center to help the staff identify and utilize house-plants with the clients.

# Indoor Container Gardening

Flowers and houseplants are not the only plants that can be grown indoors. A variety of annuals, flowering plants and herbs can be grown very successfully in containers indoors.

## Annuals

If space is limited, try growing annuals in pots indoors. It is sometimes difficult to grow annuals indoors, but it can be done! Tom Thumb zinnias, marigolds, geraniums, begonias, coleus, portulaca, mums, hot house azaleas, and miniature roses are a few of the possibilities. Other flowering plants for indoor container gardening include: Christmas cactus, African violets, cyclamen, amaryllis and bulbs such as paper white narcissus and freesias.

Flowering plants need a lot of light, a good professional potting soil, and the correct amount of water and fertilizer on a regular basis, however it is possible for the nursing home client to enjoy growing flowering plants indoors.

## Vegetable Gardening Indoors

Growing vegetables indoors may be the only option for some agencies. In many instances, the growing season can be extended for the entire year, giving clients the opportunity to enjoy produce they have grown all year round. Plenty of sunlight, good air circulation, room for growth as well as a balanced fertilizer for vegetables are all important elements for successful vegetable gardening indoors. For best results, use professional potting soils.

Spinach, lettuce, turnips, radishes, carrots, onions, garden cress, miniature tomatoes, and peppers are just a few possibilities. Herbs such as chive and parsley work well indoors (hasten germination of parsley by soaking the seeds in water overnight before planting). Alfalfa seeds or cress are easily sprouted on a piece of wet sponge. This gives the clients a sense of instant success.

Suggested planting distances and container depth for vegetables can be found on page 175.

## Vegetable Specifications

| Vegetable | Distance Apart | Container Depth |
|---|---|---|
| beets | 3" | 8" |
| broccoli | 8" | 15" |
| cabbage | 18" | 10" |
| carrots | 3" | 10" |
| corn | 10" | 8" |
| cucumbers | 16" | 8" |
| eggplant | 1 plant per 5 gallon pot | |
| herbs | 6" | 8" |
| lettuce (leaf) | 6" | 8" |
| lettuce (head) | 10" | 8" |
| melons | 1 plant per 5 gallon pot | |
| onions | 2" | 8" |
| parsley | 6" | 8" |
| peppers | 16" | 8" |
| potatoes | 2 seed pieces in a 5 gallon pot | |
| radishes | 2" | 6" |
| spinach | 5" | 6" |
| tomatoes | 1 plant in a 5 gallon pot | |
| zucchini | 1 plant in a 5 gallon pot | |

# Drying Flowers

Often clients have grown beautiful flowers which they would like to preserve. Dried and pressed materials can be made into arrangements and into various craft projects. Dried materials can add another dimension to the growing program.

## Natural Drying

Many plants dry naturally. They are harvested from the garden as soon as they feel dry when touched. Straw flowers, okra, teasel, cattails, milkweed and many grasses are examples of plants which dry naturally. Other flowers dry naturally once they have been cut. Simply place them in a container with no water.

Plants that dry naturally include:
  • baby's breath (perennial)
  • hydrangeas
  • daffodils
  • Queen Anne's lace

## Hanging Upside Down

Hanging upside down is probably the most common method for drying and preserving natural materials. Flowers from bouquets as well as those from the garden or meadows can be dried with this method.

Secure the branches of the items to be dried together with a piece of string or a rubber band. Hang them upside down suspended from a string so air can circulate all the way around the items. A dark dry room is best for drying. An attic or dark closet works well. The rubber band or string keeps the items from falling out as they dry. Most flowers will dry within 8 to 10 days. It is important that the plants be completely dry and stiff before they are taken down. The items may be sprayed with a preservative such as hair spray after they have been dried, but it is not necessary.

Some flower that can be dried using this method include:

- star flowers
- xerantheum
- dusty miller
- statice
- hydrangea
- daisies
- celosia

- calendula
- golden rod
- pussy willow
- straw flowers
- roses
- snap dragons
- asters

- carnations
- yarrow
- butterfly weed
- baby's breath
- lavender
- globe amatantha

## Sand Dried Flowers

Sand drying works well with flowers such as daisies and black-eyed Susans. The fullness of the bloom is preserved with the sand method.

Fill a cardboard box half full of dry sand. A shoe box works well. Cut off most of the stems from the freshly cut flower. Push the small stem of the flower in the sand. Sprinkle a thin layer of sand over the flowers covering the flowers completely. If the flower petals are thick, like a rose, separate the petals slightly and fill them with sand.

Place the box in a dry place for two weeks. Carefully lift the flowers out of the sand after they have dried. Make new stems for the flowers from wire and floral tape.

Commercial drying agents are available to dry flowers in the same manner as the sand drying method. Silica gel is one commercial agent available from a florist or hobby shop. Borax can be used in the same manner as sand or a combination of 1/3 borax and 2/3 cornmeal. Kitty litter can also be utilized as a drying agent.

To speed up the process, put the container in the oven. If a gas oven is utilized, the pilot light produces enough heat to dry the flowers within a few days. In an electric oven, turn the light on inside the oven. Usually flowers will dry in two to three days instead of two to three weeks.

Even though the sand method takes a bit of planning, it is a fun method to use with the clients.

Some flowers to dry this may include:

- zinnias
- roses

- black-eyed Susans
- daisies

- Queen Anne's lace

## Glycerinating Foliage

Glycernizing leaves and branches takes more effort than other methods for preserving natural items; however, it is the best method for preserving larger items.

Mix one part glycerin (available at a drug store) with two parts water. Pour about six inches of the mixture into a jar. Pound the bottoms of the stems of the items to be glycerined so they will be more absorbent. Immerse the stems in the glycerin mixture. The leaves will turn brown as they absorb the glycerin. Most materials take several weeks, but ivy can be glycerined in four or five days.

Plants that can be glycerined include:
- forsythia
- beech branches
- magnolia branches
- ivy

## Pressing

Pressed flowers can be shaped into pleasing positions before drying. Pressed flowers can be used in a variety of craft projects such as sun catchers, greeting cards, or book markers. Ferns, leaves and flowers such as violas and pansies press very nicely.

Press flowers by placing them between several layers of absorbent paper with a weight on top. An old phone book works well. Place the flower or leaf which is to be pressed on a piece of wax paper with another piece on top. Place the wax paper carefully in-between the pages of the phone book. The materials will be dried and pressed within a few days. The larger the flower or leaf the longer it will take. After removing from the paper, handle carefully as the items may be fragile.

Some plants that are good for pressing include:
- dogwood
- violets
- baby's breath
- delphiniums
- ferns
- oak leaves
- violas
- pansies
- daffodils
- Queen Anne's lace
- maple leaves

## Activities With Natural Materials

There are many craft projects which utilize natural materials, some of which are dried and others which use fresh materials. Refer to the chapter on Making Things for additional ideas.

## Tea

Fresh and dried herbs in garden plots may often be utilized in the clients' special recipes. Mint is a wonderful herb to grow in a community garden plot. It takes little care and grows year after year. Be careful with mint or it will take over the entire garden, if given a chance. Any flavor of mint grows well. A fresh sprig of mint inserted into a a glass of iced tea tastes great on a hot summer day. Apple mint is a particularly pleasant mint and it doesn't seem to take over as much as the other types of mint. Mint can be easily dried by hanging it upside down, and tea bags can be made for hot tea. A good herb shop usually carries empty tea bags which can be filled with the dried mint. This is an easy project for clients.

## Herb Butter

Another usage for herbs is herb butter. Soften butter or margarine until it is easy for the clients to mix. Chop either fresh or dried herbs which are then mixed with the butter. Refrigerate the butter until it hardens again. Spread the herbed butter on vegetables or breads. It is especially delicious on corn. Parsley, dill and basil are just a few of the herbs which are delicious when mixed in the butter.

## Potpourri

Dried flowers which are not whole or colorful enough to utilize in craft projects can be made into potpourri. Mix the petals of dried flowers together into a container, add a few drops of scent, available at herb shops or some craft stores, close the container and let season for a few days. The herb lavender is quite lovely and can be used in potpourri projects also. Cinnamon sticks and cloves make a spicy scent everyone will enjoy.

## Sachets

The scented potpourri can be sold at bazaars by the cup full or can easily be made into sachets. Cut a colorful piece of cotton material into a square about 6 by 6 inches. It does not have to be exact. Trim the edges with pinking shears. Put a small amount of the potpourri into the center, pull the edges together as the potpourri forms a ball in the bottom. Pull all the edges together to close the sachet and tie it with a colorful ribbon. They are easy to make and sell well at bazaars.

Another type of sachet can be made by cutting two squares. Turn inside out and sew the two squares together along three of the edges. Turn right side out, fill with potpourri and sew the last side shut. A bit of lace sewn around the edges will make the project appear more complete.

A third type of sachet uses a small embroidery hoop and lace. Cut two pieces of lace, fill with potpourri. Arrange the lace in the embroidery hoop, trim the hoop with a small ribbon a the top. These are great for hanging in closets or windows.

When the scent begins to fade, sprinkle a few drops of commercial scent onto the potpourri in order to refresh it.

## Tips For A Low-Cost Growing Program

- To reuse pots, sterilize the containers by washing them with diluted bleach.
- To reuse potting soil, sterilize it by baking it in an oven at 325° for approximately one hour. Although this process will not ruin a pan, it is preferable to use an old cookie sheet or cake pan.
- Always sterilize used soil and pots if they are to be reused, especially if the old plant was diseased.
- Use two quart plastic soda jugs for terrariums and pots.
- Save egg cartons, styrofoam cups and cartons, and margarine tubs for starting seeds or to catch water from containers.
- Order seeds early from seed catalogs to receive early bird discounts and bonus seeds.
- Watch for sales near the end of the season at local garden centers, especially for expensive items such as tools.

- Establish a relationship with a local garden center. They are usually willing to discuss problems and answer questions. Also, they often have seeds, flowers, plants, shrubbery and support materials such as ribbon, already made bows, wire and tape which they will be willing to discount or sell at cost.
- Call the Extension service and local garden clubs. They are often willing to donate time, money and/or supplies to assist the growing program. Don't forget to contact the local herb society too.
- To make it easier for clients to start seeds indoors, pour the seeds onto a piece of white paper which has been folded in the middle. Plant the seeds in the pots or containers by using the fold in the paper as a funnel. This works well when the seeds are too small for the clients.

The Growing Calendar of Activity Ideas which follow lists a variety of ideas which can be implemented through out the year because a growing program should not be limited to the summer months only.

## The Growing Calendar Of Activity Ideas

### January

- fresh flower arrangements from left-over flowers
- corsages
- princess pine arrangements
- show slides or films of gardens around the world
- plant lily of the valley pips or amaryllis bulbs
- review seed catalogs for spring planting
- mist house plants more frequently to increase humidity
- make pressed flower cards and suncatchers

### February

- gather seed starting supplies
- force branches by placing them in cans filled with water
- show pictures of spring branches in flower
- build bird houses
- make seed mosaics from green, pinto and lima beans, peas, sunflower and other seeds
- order seeds for garden
- late February begin broccoli, cauliflower, cabbage and brussel sprout seeds indoors

### March

- replant house plants
- start cuttings from house plants
- start narcissus bulbs in shallow container with pebbles
- plant herb seeds indoors such as parsley, lavender or basil
- start plants indoors for outdoor garden—i.e., tomatoes, peppers
- begin soil preparation in outdoor garden
- plan outdoor garden plots

- transplant broccoli, cauliflower and cabbage into larger pots, keep
      them in a sunny area
- in early April, plant cool season vegetables in the garden such as
      radishes, peas, carrots, onions and lettuce
- start summer flowering bulbs in pots with soil—place in a cool room
      (cannas, dahlias, tuberous begonias)

## April

- continue preparing the soil by adding organic matter
      (peat moss, manure or compost) and a balanced fertilizer (5-10-5)
- plant broccoli, cauliflower and brussel sprouts outside, but watch for hard frosts
- go for a wildflower walk in late April
- cut flowering branches and bring them indoors for arrangements
      (apple, pear, cherry, forsythias, etc.)
- visit a spring garden show

## May

- plant annuals in hanging baskets and containers for outdoors
- take cuttings from the mum plants that arrived for Easter—root them
      in a either water or soil
- gather flowers from dogwood trees for pressing and drying
- visit nursery, garden center to make purchases
- transplant seedlings to outdoors
- plant rest of garden in late May
- weeding and care of outdoor garden
- have a strawberry festival
- pick wildflowers for pressing and drying

## June

- move houseplants outdoors for the summer
- apply a weed control mulch to the garden (black plastic, straw, newspaper, etc)
- visit local flower gardens
- plant late summer flowers
- more weeding and caring for garden
- begin harvesting early crops
- cut back poinsettias up to 50 percent—repot and keep them in a sunny
      location, fertilize regularly
- pick pansies, violas for pressing

## July

- water, weed and fertilize the garden
- pinch back mums until July 15th, then let them grow
- pinch back annuals as needed
- use flowers/herbs from garden for sensory activities

- plant late summer flowers
- make flower arrangements from garden flowers
- visit fruit farm for peach season
- pick Queen Anne's lace for pressing and drying

## August

- visit a garden of annual flowers
- start gathering flowers to be dried
- harvest goodies from garden
- hold a harvest luncheon or dinner for all gardeners
- nature activities—color, texture, shape, tree identification cards

## September

- gather pine cones, acorns, grasses, teasel, mill weed and other materials for drying
- dry flowers from garden
- buy bulbs early for best selection
- spray houseplants against bugs and bring them inside
- dry sunflower heads
- take an overnight camping trip
- build bird feeders

## October

- cut leaves and branches as they turn colors—glycerinize for use
      in decorations and arrangements
- press leaves for stationery, placecards
- begin dark treatment for poinsettias
- plant fall bulbs
- dig up dahlias, cannas and tuberous begonia bulbs for winter storage
- visit fruit farm for apple season
- make dried flower arrangements
- harvest mums and marigolds for Halloween party decorations
- hold a barn party
- carve harvested pumpkins
- put out bird feeders
- start feeding birds with sunflower, squash and pumpkin seeds
- go on a fall foliage trip

## November

- start grass seed Christmas trees from pinecones
      (soak pinecones in water, remove, cover with grass seed, mist daily with water)
- make pressed flower Christmas cards
- make pinecone and burlap Christmas wreaths

**December**

- make name tags with pressed flowers for Christmas tea
- make dried Christmas critters
- decorate Norfolk Island Pines
- build snow people
- decorate Christmas trees with dried Queen Anne's lace and bows
- decorate pinecone Christmas trees

# Resources

Allison, L. (1975). *The Reasons for the Seasons*. Boston, MA: Little, Brown and Company.

Burlingame, A. W. (1974). *Hoe for Health*. Birmingham, MI: Alice W. Burlingame.

Fiarotta, P. (1975). *Snips and Snails and Walnut Whales*. New York, NY: Workman Publishing.

van der Smissen, B. and Goering, O.H. (1965). *Nature-Oriented Activities*. Ames, IA: Iowa State University Press.

# SPECIAL EVENTS

# SPECIAL EVENTS

Special events add excitement to the recreation program.  They often interest clients who prefer to stay in their rooms to become a part of the recreation program.  Special events can also be used to foster challenges through competition or as an opportunity for the clients to be performers.

Although some agencies might consider bingo, movies and games activities as special events because they involve a large number of clients, they should be considered as large group activities.  Large group events might be those which are held on a fairly regular basis of at least once a month and involve a larger percentage of clients.  In some agencies a large group may be twenty while in others, a group would not be considered to be large unless there were more than thirty clients participating.

Special events tend to involve a theme which often relates to a holiday.  This certainly makes it easier for the staff and clients to focus their thinking in order to create an appropriate program, decorations, and refreshments.  The number of special events that an agency offers will depend on the number of clients, resources available and the time of year.  At the very least, one special program should be planned per month.

Outings into the community which might be considered as a special event will be covered in a later section, as they present a variety of challenges to the staff different from the ones for special events.

## Making An Event Special

Special events should be just what the title suggests.  There may even be an event which is exclusive to members of a certain club.  It is important to provide equal amounts of attention to each unit or group;  however, it does make an event special if the person has received a personalized invitation.

One agency visited by the authors had to hold a birthday party every week for their clientele because everyone attended all of the parties.  There was no room in the schedule for any other events after conducting a birthday party every week and there was nothing special about the party as everyone always went to each party.  Another agency held picnics on the patio for the same group of clients once a week. They simply took the clients' lunch tray out onto the patio.  Both of these programs lack the excitement which should be associated with a special event.

Sometimes an event needs to be scheduled more than once in order to accommodate all of the clients who should participate.  Issuing invitations for specific dates for holding the event by wings may be more appropriate than having everyone attend at once.  For example, a 600 bed facility used to hold an annual picnic for the clients.  An hour-and-a-half was need to transport clients to the event and by that time, many of the clients were ready to return to their rooms.  The solution was to hold a picnic for each wing involving fewer clients each time.  Because it took less time to transport, the clients were able to participate in the preparation of the meal, play some games and eat before returning to their rooms.  For an event to be a special event, it must be something out of the ordinary and involve an appropriate number of clients.

# Planning And Preparation

These events are an important part of any recreation program and deserve adequate preparation time. They are only one part of the program, however, and recreation professionals should be cautioned about spending too much time in planning and preparation. Too often the staff spend weeks developing decorations, entertainment and refreshments with little if any assistance or input from the clients.

## Client Involvement

Special events take on more meaning when the clients have assisted in the planning and preparation. The anticipation factor of the experience is heightened whenever small group experiences have been used as building blocks toward the major event. Small groups of clients can make decorations, create food items and even create and deliver special invitations. Another small group of clients can write an article for the client newspaper or develop flyers to advertise the event. On the actual day of the event clients can be designated as official greeters to welcome other guests.

Client involvement will take more communicating and coordinating by the various staff members; however, the number of client oriented activities which are generated make this effort worthwhile.

## Refreshments

A word of caution on food. Although the clients would love a feast at every event, it is not necessary to provide banquet fare each time. Special meals do make nice special activities and should be scheduled; however, every event should not be a meal.

## Storage and Reuse of Program Items

An important consideration when developing the material for a special event is the ability to re-use the decorations and items. If they can be used on another occasion, then storage has to be considered. Since storage space is often at a premium, the need to create elaborate three dimensional items should receive careful attention. If the amount of space for client seating is limited, decorations should not limit seating further. A three dimensional palm tree may look beautiful, but if the clients cannot see the entertainment or find a seat because of the tree, then it is best not to use it as decoration.

# Special Event Suggestions

Following are some special events program suggestions which have been utilized with all levels of clientele. They are meant to be idea generators and may be modified for most agencies. Each event is accompanied by suggestions for planning and programming a variety of activities. Client involvement in the planning process will help make every event special.

## Picnics

Arrange for smaller picnics by wing or unit in order to provide an experience which is more than just going outside to eat.  Make arrangements for the event with the nursing director in residential facilities to determine the best day of the week for nursing.  Invite the nursing staff to attend and participate in all of the activities.

Plan a special menu with the dietary staff and try to provide foods that even those on puree diets can enjoy as a special treat.  Activities such as vegetable printing should be set up for those who arrive early.  Newsprint paper can be stretched across the table and the clients can make their own place settings by dipping sliced vegetables such as carrots and potatoes, or even fruits such as apples and oranges in tempera paint and printing on the paper (refer to Chapter 17, Making Things, for additional directions).  Even clients who are confused and/or disoriented will enjoy creating the table covers.  Games such as quoit golf or egg toss are familiar and can easily be played while others arrive (refer to Chapter 18, Homemade Games and Chapter 14, Activities That Promote Exercise).  A giant sing-a-long is a great activity for clients prior to enjoying a picnic feast.  Color or texture cards can easily be used by a volunteer or staff member at the table.  Leaf drawings can be matched with actual leaves that a volunteer has placed on the table (refer to Chapter 12, Sensory Awareness).

Clients can be encouraged to assist with the actual meal by rolling silverware in napkins, passing out condiments, and setting the table.  The activities should be held prior to eating because the clients prefer to eat and immediately return to their rooms.  Adding activities to a picnic will enrich the experience for the client as well as for the staff and volunteers who attend.

## Petting Zoo

Pets can motivate a client to come out of his/her room when nothing else seems to work.  A petting zoo on the lawn or in the parking lot will encourage clients to leave their room and in many cases walk a greater distance than normal.  The 4-H clubs do an excellent job with providing a variety of pets as well as a group of children who care for the pets.

Since children can be as motivating as pets, the combination is sure to draw a crowd.  The 4-H group may even be able to provide fencing so there would be no worry about the pets escaping or clients wandering.  The 4-H club will vary the pets to include ducks, calves, lambs, and young goats as well as the normal kittens and puppies.  Contact the county extension office and speak with the 4-H agent to determine if there is a group that would be willing to bring their animals.

The humane society is often a good source for pets, particularly cats and dogs.  They are often willing to visit on a monthly basis all year long.

The staff are also a good source for pets.  Many agencies have successfully held staff pet shows.  Another approach to the staff members sharing their friendly pets with the clients is to have an individual staff member bring in his/her pet during his/her shift.  The recreation personnel takes the pet from room to room to visit.  This avoids the confusion associated with many pets and staff members together.  The pet may tire more quickly than the clients, so a careful eye must be kept on the animal.

Often agencies have resident pets which relate very well with the clients. However, a word of caution about obtaining too many pets. If the staff have to spend large blocks of time taking care of the pets, instead of being with the clients, there are too many pets. Also the pet should be there for the clients, not the staff. A cat which won't leave the area behind the nurses desk is not helpful to the clients.

## Parades

Everyone loves a parade and although it is often impractical to take the clients to view a parade, it is possible to hold one within the agency. Clients can dress in costumes, wheelchairs and walkers can be decorated for the occasion and floats can easily be created out of carts and wheelchairs. Music is provided by a tape recorder with help from kitchen instruments and kazoos. Clients parade up and down the halls singing songs and stopping to do dance routines, or tell stories and jokes, at the various lounges. The participants in the parade can even have their own party after the parade as a "thank you" for participating. Parades are especially appropriate on such holidays as Memorial day, the Fourth of July and Easter. They provide entertainment for all of the clients, even those who don't leave their room, and take little staff effort to plan and run. A brownie troop or even a small marching unit from the community might be persuaded to join in the fun. Toy fire trucks and horses can be used to represent small scale versions of the real things featured in a parade.

On a larger scale, a fire truck, old cars and the local bands could be invited to the facility for a parade around the grounds. In conjunction with a bazaar, carnival or ice cream social which the community is invited to attend, a large parade is feasible. It would have to be scheduled far in advance and not near a traditional holiday as the bands, troops and fire trucks are busy on those days.

## Christmas Caroling

The same parade idea works really well for Christmas with caroling. The clients can enjoy a moment of stardom and a sense of accomplishment as they carol through the halls.

## Pioneer Crafts Festival

This special event takes extensive planning and should be open to the public as well as the clients and their families. An event for the public can bring positive publicity to the facility and do a lot toward goodwill within the community.

Clients can be involved in the planning and coordination of this event. The local crafts society or crafts persons should be contacted to arrange a date. The program should be set up so that old time crafts are demonstrated by craft people. Sales of their items may be possible to the general public. Clients with similar skills will enjoy being matched up with a crafts person for the afternoon. Such activities as blacksmithing, spinning, weaving, broom making, quilting, tinsmithing, chair caning, quilling, needlework and pottery would be a few of the activities. Even such household skills as butter churning, soap and candle making could be demonstrated. Homemade soup could be sold or a corn roast held as a part of the festival.

It is best to demonstrate skills which are familiar to the clients and are common to the area. This is an excellent time to hold a flea market or to sell craft items. The media will want to publicize the event so be sure to contact the newspaper, radio and television studios early.

## Carnival

Carnivals can be held either indoors, in a picnic area, grassy spot or the parking lot. The sense of adventure from an outdoor carnival makes it an obvious choice. The booths can be run by volunteers such as girl or boy scouts. This combines the fun of a carnival with the joy and enthusiasm of young people.

One of the nicest things about a carnival is that it takes the familiar actions the clients use in other activities and puts them into practice. For example, the basketball toss or bean bag throws are always part of a carnival. Even bowling skills can be part of the carnival fun when the clients roll a ball up a ramp and into a muffin tin or box. Carnival activities don't have to be complicated to be fun. See Chapter 18, Homemade Games, for ideas.

Dropping clothespins into a plastic jug is easy to coordinate, yet a challenge for the participants. The activities should include a variety of skills such as rolling, tossing, dropping, kicking, and spinning so that not just one action (such as throwing) is repeated over and over. Clients love activities such as throwing a wet sponge at a popular staff person. At one carnival, the clients tossed the bowling pin into a box while the bowling balls were utilized in another game. It simply takes imagination to turn ordinary skills and games into a carnival of events. A few muffin tins, Ping-Pong™ balls, tennis and rubber balls, boxes and coffee cans can make enough activities to keep everyone entertained for an afternoon (refer to Chapter 18 for Homemade Games).

Helium balloons add a festive touch to the occasion and can be provided with relatively little expense if the staff purchase the balloons, rent the helium tank and blow them up themselves. The costs can even be deferred by asking the clients to pay twenty-five cents per balloon. It is best not to have a traditional balloon release. In many states balloon releases are now prohibited because of harmful environmental effects.

One of the nicest things about a carnival is that the clients can stay as long as they like, playing the various games and then move on at their own pace. This is good for the client who only likes to attend for short periods of time.

If prizes are awarded, it is desirable to set up a prize table near the end of the carnival so clients can select their own prizes. They might win colored slips of paper at each of the booths that can be traded in for prizes at the table. Some prizes would be worth more slips than others so the clients have a variety of ways to use their earnings.

## Triathlon

Instead of running three physically taxing activities in a row such as the traditional triathlon, have five events scheduled over a five day period. Each client selects three in which he/she will participate. There might be three physical activities such as an obstacle course, basketball toss and discus (Frisbee™) throw and two mental activities such as checkers and a spelling bee from which to select. The variety of activities permits a wider range of clients to enter the events.

It is not necessary to require the clients to enter three events and the staff might decide teams are more appropriate. In this case, one person enters the bowling competition while another team member competes in horseshoes and the third in Velcro™ darts. Some of the activities should be selected from familiar games. Dominoes, shuffleboard or bocci ball may be on the schedule or clients may select activities which were created for this event such as the obstacle course, or the water pistol competition.

An awards banquet could be held and the prizes awarded to the winners. Everyone should receive an award for participation. Awards can be made very inexpensively by using paper purchased by the pound. Involve the clients beforehand by having one trace circles on the paper using a drinking glass for a pattern. Another can cut the circles out with pinking shears. The ribbon from funeral flowers can be ironed and cut (using pinking shears) by another client. The ribbon is then taped to the back of the paper disk. The name of the event and the date should be written in by the staff members. The first, second and third place awards can be made in the same manner. These simple awards will become prized possessions. Along with a certificate or a ribbon the winners might win a T-shirt. It is not difficult to silkscreen a pattern on the T-shirt and they will also become prized possessions.

## Theme Parties

It is sometimes easier for the staff and clients to be more creative when they help determine a theme. Working with a theme gives the group a sense of direction. An idea for a theme can be developed by a discussion or reminiscence group. Activities, decoration and foods for the event should be based on the theme. An event can be on a large scale and involve most of the staff programming efforts for a month with a culminating activity, or it might be one afternoon or an evening event. In either instance, the theme might be "school days" with the decorations from an old school house. The activities could be a spelling bee, alphabet games and a math contest. Pages from old text books can be copied so the program is run just like school in a one room school house. Apple slices could be served as "lunch." The kindergarten or first grade class from a local school could become involved too.

A more elaborate event might include the entire facility in a month long cruise. Decorations would include paper portholes, life preservers and railings for each unit. Activities for the month could be those found on board the ship such as bingo, shuffleboard, shopping, casino night, movies, cocktail parties and dancing. A staff/client talent show might be part of the night club activities. A special program could be scheduled to represent each port of call. This event takes a lot of cooperation between all of the departments, but really aids in building a team approach to programming.

Holiday parties are usually easy to plan, but for months like August, with no holidays, the staff might have a Mexican festival, a campfire program, or a hoedown. A calendar which lists national days such as National Ice Cream Day or Mardi Gras provides a variety of ideas for programs. Even local customs can become idea generators for special event programming.

## Birthday Parties

Although the monthly birthday party only involves a small percentage of the clients on any given month, by the end of the year everyone has been involved. Therefore, they are included under the discussion of special events. One of the goals of the agency is to provide as normal an experience for the client as is possible. Looking at a birthday party for adults, one usually finds cake, ice cream, conversation and few games. Unfortunately, in nursing homes, birthday parties seem to center around games and cake because the clients do not usually hold conversations with one another.

A way to make the birthday party a more personal experience is to invite each person who is having a birthday that month to a party in his/her honor. The invitation should be in a written format, possibly silkscreened by the clients, and delivered to the guests. Each birthday person is invited to bring a specific number of guests. The guests may be other residents or family members. In many facilities space is a problem, so the party is limited to the birthday person and two guests. A special buffet dinner is provided from the dietary department and is served in a room away from the other clients. This makes the program special and an event to look forward to whenever a person is invited.

The menu may consist of the client's favorite foods. In many cases this may include a local favorite such as chicken-and-biscuits or fried oysters. At least two choices of entrees should be included along with all of the side dishes. This is one event when diets are usually forgotten. Often the guests of the birthday recipient will assist the client with any food which needs to be cut, or fed to the client thus reducing the amount of staff required.

The program would include an introduction of each of the birthday guests even if everyone knows each other. Each guest of honor is to tell how old he/she is and relate a favorite birthday experience or present. If the client cannot answer, the family member or guest will usually have a short story to relate. The stories should be told before the traditional singing of happy birthday. A small gift from the agency may be provided. A fresh flower or a helium balloon for each recipient makes a simple yet appropriate reminder of the special day.

## Newcomer's Tea

Clients new to the facility should be made to feel welcome through a personal invitation to a tea for all new comers. Once a month is usually often enough to hold such an event. The program should be scheduled in the afternoon. More of the administrative staff would be able to attend the event if it is held later in the day.

Family members can be invited to attend the program so the client feels more comfortable. Light refreshments can be served and the staff should be introduced to the new clients. The new clients should also introduce themselves. A welcoming committee of clients who have been in the facility for a while should be invited in order to answer any questions from the client's point of view. If the facility has developed a slide program or a video production about the agency it might be shown, or a special program developed by the clients with welcoming messages might be used. A production such as the one developed by the clients would be more personal as well as making use of the creative abilities of the current clients. It is important for the agency's administrator to be represented either in person or via the film at the newcomer's program.

## Home Movies, Videos and Slides

Slides and videos of various programs can become a special event for the clients. Taking slides or videos of fishing trips then putting them together can be the entertainment for the annual fish fry. Such a presentation adds to the recall phase of the program. Often clients won't be able to recognize themselves on the big screen and will truly enjoy the experience of seeing themselves in the movies.

Videos and slides of special programs and outings can be used to encourage other clients to attend the next time. Some agencies are able to broadcast programs into the clients room. One agency broadcast a short bible service, exercise program and a current events session which reminds everyone of the events for the day as well as upcoming special programs. This goes out over the internal television system and clients are able to tune in on their television sets. Other agencies are able to utilize intercom systems in much the same manner.

Clients can even be encouraged to write their own stories and produce movies. If the clients aren't quite ready to write their own movies, they can begin by creating videos about the agency. They can be interviewed about their favorite aspect of the agency and even take the video on location and film such things as the dietary and laundry departments in operation. After completing a tour of the agency and various client interviews, they will probably be ready to film short skits of themselves engaging in activities. Such productions make interesting programs for an easily planned special event.

### Family Afternoons

Programs should be scheduled which give family members an opportunity to participate with their relative. Often family members will act as volunteers with special programs or outings, but that is usually a small percentage of families. Often relatives don't know what to talk about when they come to visit their older person. Having an event they can take their relative to during their visit gives the family something to do together.

The programs should be such that people can stop by, participate for a short time, then leave. Concerts with refreshments, an art show, even a petting zoo or a craft display can provide a family experience. Even holiday dinners can provide an opportunity for the family to enjoy a special time together. One agency asked staff members to volunteer on Thanksgiving in order to serve a special turkey dinner to the family and clients. The family members each paid a small fee to pay for the food. The event was held with their own families. The event became so popular there were two seatings with one hundred people per seating. The dinner gave the families the opportunity to be together without the problems associated with transporting clients to their homes. If the event is held at the noon meals, the staff members are still able to enjoy an evening meal with their families.

Following are some additional programming ideas which might be scheduled on the afternoon or evening when a large number of family members visit so they too can be involved in the experience.

### Smile Contest

Set up a small area which acts as a studio. Mount a 35mm camera on a tripod to make the experience seem like that of a professional photographer's studio. Set-up appointments so that the clients have their photograph taken immediately after having their hair styled or their hair and/or beard trimmed.

A local photography shop will often provide the agency with a discount on the developing costs. They will be willing to do the developing for less if the photographs are black and white. The photographs should be at least 5" x 7" so they are easy to see. The photos should be framed even if the frame is made from paper by the clients.

The photographs might be hung in a prominent place where visitors, clients and staff can easily view them. Each photo is numbered in a corner where it is easily seen. A ballot box with pencils and ballots placed in a prominent place is also necessary. A series of categories listed on the ballot such as the cutest smile, the silliest grin, the best upside down smile will insure that a large number of different clients will win awards. Paper ribbons can be attached to the photographs after the votes have been tallied. A long weekend of Thursday through Monday is probably enough to gather the votes. The photographs with the ribbons should remain hung for a few more days so the clients can show off their awards. It is not necessary for everyone to win an award as each client will be given his/her photograph.

The photographs can easily be displayed in the client's room after the contest. They can be a great help to a new staff member or volunteer who has not learned everyone's name.

Photographs can also be used to remind confused clients where their room is located. An older photograph such as one when the client was 50 to 60 years old is usually more recognizable to the client than one from the present.

An idea similar to the smile contest can be used with silhouettes. A staff member hangs a piece of white paper on the wall. The client sits in a chair facing to one side about one foot away from the paper. A light on a stand about ten feet from the wall is used to throw the shadow of the person's profile on the paper. A staff member draws around the profile and labels the drawing immediately so it does not become confused with others. Cut out the silhouettes and mount them on dark construction paper. Everyone's profile should be displayed for a time period so family and friends can see the silhouette.

## Art Show

If there is a client with art talent, a one-person show of his/her previous and current work makes an excellent activity for friends and families. The media also enjoy publicizing such an event. The crafts from the arts and crafts classes is another way to feature an art show. Murals painted with vegetable or sponge printings done on newsprint can also be displayed as a part of a show. One professional encouraged his clients to draw the worst possible portrait of him so they would feel comfortable being creative. The clients really enjoyed the experience and even consented to having the sketches displayed for everyone to see.

## Who's That Baby, or Wedding Photos

Photographs from weddings and/or baby pictures make a great display for visitors to enjoy with clients. An element of surprise can be added by asking the clients, visitors and staff to match the clients with their photographs. The person who identifies the greatest number of people correctly may win a certificate or a small item made by the clients.

Paraphernalia from the client's younger days (which are usually collectibles by today's standards) can be brought in and put on display. Of course, security should be of concern with an event such as this. Old high button shoes, a shoe hook, old hats and even kitchen items such as a potato masher will be conversation starters with the group. Items can be categorized to relate to such things as the kitchen, old tools, clothing, school days, etc.

## Fashion Show

If the agency receives a lot of donated clothing, fashion shows may be scheduled on a regular basis. Many agencies who do not receive donated clothing have held fashion shows with vintage clothing and/or wedding gowns. Men can even get involved with old time clothing and suits.

Having a stage set up so the clients parade or wheel around in front of the others is essential. An afternoon tea adds an extra touch to the event. A fashion show is a great activity for a women's group or another club that needs an activity.

### Happy Hour/Tail Gates/Super Bowl Parties

Even if the agency has a policy against alcohol, juices and sodas can be served at a Happy Hour or cocktail party. Happy Hour parties are a great way to celebrate a late Friday afternoon or early evening. The staff, as well as the clients, are usually tired by Friday afternoon and would rather hide in their offices or rooms. A Happy Hour program with some light music gives clients a chance to get out of their rooms for some socializing and also gives the staff members a pleasant activity for late in the week.

Parties to celebrate the start of a football game or to cheer on their team for the world series are easily coordinated. Picnic foods or simple snack foods such as potato chips or peanuts can be provided, along with a large screen television set for viewing. Activities before the game should relate to the sport. For example, if the game is football, how many new words is it possible to make from the word FOOTBALL. The people then select which team they want to support, to foster competition between the two groups.

## Toward More Innovative Special Events

The ideas for special events are limited only by the organizer's imagination. Many events take little planning and yield great results. Some special events should be held where the clients provide the entertainment and some should be outside entertainers. When there is innovative planning, long time clients never tire of attending special events.

## Resources

Merrill, T. (1967). *Activities for the Aged and Infirm.* Springfield, IL: Charles C. Thomas Publishers.

# NOTES

# TRIPS AND OUTINGS

# TRIPS AND OUTINGS

Outings into the community can be very valuable to the client who resides in a residential facility. Often an outing is seen as a link with the local community and can alleviate the sense of being trapped in the home. Outings can also be sensory stimulating, of reminiscent value, and challenging for the clients. The breath of fresh air and a chance to be in different surroundings is often motivating to the client. Outings can often be viewed as a mini-vacation from daily life.

## Making The Outing Enjoyable

Outings require some special provisions and supervision to ensure that the client has a safe and enjoyable experience. It is important to keep clients from becoming too tired or overstimulated.

### Informing the Participants

The various phases of the recreation experience are easily applied to trip and outing activities. An understanding of what the clients might be experiencing during each phase of the experience will aid the staff in planning.

The first phase is *anticipation*. Clients want to know the schedule for the trip. Departure times as well as return times should be explained. Clients prefer this information in writing. Reassurance that the doctor has approved their attendance on the outing is vital for most residential facilities. Doctor's approval is sometimes the key to motivating a client to venture out of the home to enjoy the experience. They often need reassurance that restroom facilities and assistance will be readily available.

Another major concern is money. Arrangements should be made prior to the event concerning money. In many cases this might mean obtaining some spending money from the business office for the clients while in others it might mean reassuring the client that money is not necessary.

Clients should be given some notice about an outing, but no more than one and a half weeks. They tend to worry if there is a greater length of time involved between the invitation and the actual experience. At times this may not be feasible, but expect a larger number of last minute cancellations if the clients are invited too early.

### Travel Arrangements

The *travel phase* of the recreation experience should be kept as short as possible. The vehicle or vehicles utilized for the experience must be prepared and waiting for the clients to board. If it takes longer than fifteen minutes to get the vehicle loaded and away from the facility there are either too many people going on the trip or too many last minute details. The loading of the vehicle must be completed with as much ease as possible. Providing an enjoyable experience for the client is the most important factor, therefore, the number of people per trip should be limited.

Every outing should begin with a greeting and an announcement that the event is beginning. It is also helpful to remind clients of the itinerary. Travel should be less than one hour and as short as possible for clients who are slightly confused or are a bit fretful about attending. Clients experience fewer symptoms of motion sickness and less need to use restrooms when the driving time is kept short.

## Event Selection

The *actual experience* should always last longer than the travel time. If it took an hour to get to the event and the performance is forty five minutes in length, then the staff must supplement the event with either more activity or a snack stop. On the other hand, if clients have a reduced attention span and a program is more than two hours in length, then it is definitely too long. The length of the experience is somewhat determined by the health of the client. Clients who have been on outings before, are mentally alert, and utilize wheelchairs will usually outlast everyone. The alert and ambulatory client will need more rest stops than the wheelchair client.

The actual experience should be something that older adults would enjoy. Often free tickets are made available to older adults. Caution must be taken when accepting such donations because the performance may not be age appropriate or of interest to older adults. Kiddie carnivals and avant-garde theatre performances are more appealing to a younger or more sophisticated audience.

There is often a tendency to load up a bus, take clients for a drive, eat something on the bus and return to the facility. This is an easy way out for the staff! Remember, the experience is for the clients and they are often not able to absorb much about the area as the vehicle travels down the road. Often because of seating arrangements there may be limited visibility; therefore, there should be more to the experience than a bus ride with a snack.

The group may be interested in taking a trip to view the fall colors or a tour of the community to see Christmas lights. Even a driving tour outing can be made more enjoyable for the clients by a stop at a fruit stand to look at pumpkins or a stop by the skating rink to watch the skaters. The trip should be broken up with stops to look at vistas even if the group is not capable of getting off of the vehicle.

One agency takes 100 clients on a bus ride then out to eat a meal twice a year. The staff spends more time in the restrooms and assisting clients on and off the buses than they do interacting with the clients. There is little therapeutic value to such an experience. Smaller groups on more frequently scheduled excursions is not only more personal, but of greater value to the participants.

## Combining Events

It is best to avoid outings where the clients have to get off the bus more than twice. Loading procedures are tiring for clients as well as staff. Therefore, plan experiences which combine activities at each stop. Fishing at a lake with a picnic lunch; a cookout breakfast with sensory activities; a band concert with a snack; or a visit to a farm with feed for the animals. Events do not necessarily need to be combined in order to be a complete experience for the clients. A musical, a beauty contest or a trip to a carnival or fair can stand alone, especially if the event will be held in the evening.

Clients usually need to use the restroom upon arrival at a destination. It is often valuable to park the vehicle near the restrooms until the clients have disembarked.

Clients usually prefer daytime excursions to evening events, so there is often a need to include lunch with the experience. The type of menu served should take into account the program and facilities. If the group is touring a commercial facility and using the agency's grounds, a simple picnic lunch is in order.  If the group is using a park pavilion for the day, then a more elaborate cookout could be planned.  Clients should assist in the preparation and serving of the meal whenever possible.

Someone from the staff should always visit the facility prior to the event to assess the amenities.  Since the staff is trained to look for things such as curbs, doors which are too small for wheelchairs and poor lighting, a staff member should be the one to do an initial assessment of a facility.  Consider all aspects of the experience during this review, including such factors as where the clients will sit, where the vehicle should be unloaded, and whether or not sun hats will be needed.

## Site Accessibility

Failure to adequately check out the site prior to the experience can turn a pleasant outing into an unhappy experience.  Staff should know beforehand how many steps are involved if there are curbs or uneven sidewalks, and the location and accessability of the restroom facilities.

Failure to personally check out a site resulted in a "few steps" turning out to be 23 steps on one of the authors' earliest outing experiences.  The Trip Resources Assessment checklist [Figure 17, p. 201] in the last section of this chapter was designed to assist staff in determining the accessibility of a facility and resources of a prospective site for an outing.

Although it is desirable, there are no perfectly accessible facilities when the group leaves the facility.  Consider this as a challenge for the staff and clients rather than as a reason to avoid outings.  Of course, it is advisable to rule out totally inaccessible facilities.  Many times substitute experiences will provide the desired results.  Taking clients to a major league ball game was an expensive once a year venture for one nursing home.  They discovered that the clients enjoyed going to a local game only twenty minutes away.  Because there were fewer people in attendance the clients could take up as much room as they desired.  The bleacher aisles were roomier, lawn chairs were permitted, it was easier to park wheelchairs and the restrooms were closer.  The clients enjoyed this experience more than the major league game as they could get to games more often, they did not have to pay an entrance fee and they got home earlier in the evening.

The *travel home* phase should be kept as short as possible because the clients are usually tired and want to get back as quickly as possible.  For this reason, it is best to take the shortest way back.  Remember, limit the amount of driving time to under one hour when planning an outing.

## The Return Trip

The last phase in any recreation experience is recall.  For many clients this phase actually begins during the travel home phase.  Encouraging clients to reminisce about the outing during the ride home enhances this phase of the experience.

At the end of the trip, make a statement to sum up the experience for clients.  For example, "it's always nice to go on a trip, but it sure is good to be back home again" helps clients realize the experience is over and that they are once again at their residence.  Slightly disoriented clients may be confused upon their return home, and a positive comment helps remind them that this is indeed their home.  This slight disorientation should not deter staff from taking these clients on additional outings.  A client's behavior on the vehicle going to the site and while at the site should be the deciding factor.  Those who cry, moan, or act out should only be taken on very short excursions.

## Recalling the Experience

Many clients will recall certain aspects of the experience over and over. Writing articles for the newspaper, discussing the experience in reminiscence groups or with the other personnel enhances the recall phase. Momentos from the experience may also be important to clients. Little things such as a duck feather or a program might be what the client elects to save. The recreation staff must help the client determine appropriate items for souvenirs (one client, on an outing to a fruit farm, decided to take a glass of apple cider for a souvenir). At times, the recreation staff must gently remind the client that an item might spoil or would be better if left at the site.

Other resident staff members should be informed about the adventures the clients experienced on their outing. A post trip report informs other departments about the experience and permits the recreation personnel to reflect on the outing so it may be revised for future events. On one outing, nursing home residents had the privilege of petting a two day old lion cub. They were so thrilled about the experience they went home and told everyone they had petted a lion. They failed to mention how young the lion was, so everyone had an image of a huge full-grown lion. The nursing staff knew the recreation personnel would never let the clients near a full grown lion let alone give them the opportunity to pet one; therefore they began to worry about the orientation of some of the clients. The post trip report which was sent to the nursing staff immediately following the experience cleared up the confusion. A trip report helps to keep everyone involved in the experience and not just the few staff members who participated. It is also a valuable tool for communicating with the administrator about what occurred while the group was away from the facility.

Outings into the community can add excitement to the recreation schedule and should be a part of the recreational opportunities available to clients on a regular basis.

## Outing Destinations And Ideas

The following suggestions for outing possibilities are intended to assist recreation personnel in making trips and outings an enjoyable addition to their client-oriented program.

Community Activities
- organization sponsored dinners
- restaurants
- local tourist attractions
- shopping malls
- flea markets
- community festivals/fairs
- carnivals

Cultural
- theatre productions
- concerts, plays, musicals
- band concerts at the park
- local beauty pageants

Historical
- historic sites
- train rides
- antique machine shows
- museums with special programs

## Outdoor-Related

- day camp at a camp
- overnight camping
- cookout breakfast at a park
- campfire program
- sportsman's show
- nature center tours
- wildlife preserve
- gardens
- park—hikes, kite flying

## Farm/Animal-Oriented

- working farm
- farmer's market
- county fair
- annual farm show
- zoo
- horse farm
- fruit farm

## Tours

- fast food restaurant tours
- television studio tours
- fruit farms
- factories—pretzel/potato chip/ candy, etc.
- fall leaves excursions

## Sports

- local adult baseball games
- little league games
- high school football games

## Water-Related

- boat cruises
- pontoon boating
- fishing
- wading/splashing

## Winter-Oriented

- Christmas lights tour
- Christmas shopping
- observe ice skating or downhill skiing
- watch ice break up on a river
- sleigh rides

# Staffing An Outing

Outings take special planning and consideration between the various disciplines. The following materials have been prepared to help ensure safe and successful outings into the community.

# Trip Resources Assessment

The Trip Resources Assessment checklist [Figure 17] on the following page will be useful when determining program resources and accessibility factors relating to a proposed outing destination. A qualified recreation staff member should personally visit the site to administer the assessment.

**Trip Resources Assessment**

Assessment Date _____ Trip Date _____

Agency _____

Address _____
       Street, P. O. Box                City                   State        Zip

Contact Person _____Title _____Phone _____

Size of Group_____ Cost _____(group) (each) Preferred Times _____

Directions _____

_____

Emergencies _____
              Phone numbers, Hospitals, etc.

Program _____ Length _____ Description _____

_____

**Comments**

Type: |___|___|___|___|___|___|
     unstructured       structured

Participation: |___|___|___|___|___|___|
     entertainment     education

**Skill Level**
Social: |___|___|___|___|___|___|
   low       high

Physical: |___|___|___|___|___|___|
   low       high

Cognitive: |___|___|___|___|___|___|
   low       high

**Physical Setting**
Rest Rooms: |___|___|___|___|___|___|
   none      wheelchair accessible

Eating Area: |___|___|___|___|___|___|
   none      wheelchair accessible

Steps: |___|___|___|___|___|___|
   many    none   wheelchair ramps

Seating: |___|___|___|___|___|___|
   none      seats with backs

Walks/Trails |___|___|___|___|___|___|
   none      wheelchair accessible

Terrain: |___|___|___|___|___|___|
   hilly      flat

Shelter: |___|___|___|___|___|___|
   none      enclosed

Water Fountains: |___|___|___|___|___|___|
   none      wheelchair accessible

Lighting |___|___|___|___|___|___|
   none      adequate

**Figure 17**  Trip Resources Assessment Form

## Planning The Trip

The steps necessary to planning a safe and enjoyable outing follow. The information needed for the trip should be documented in writing and attached to a copy of the Trip Resource Assessment form. A copy should be kept in the trip file to simplify the planning process when the trip is repeated.

    I. Trip Information
- event
- date
- time of departure and return
- destination
- route information, traveling time, directions

   II. Trip Objectives

  III. Client Information
- number of spaces available on the vehicle
- number of clients attending
- number of wheelchair/ ambulatory clients attending
- number of clients with special needs or needing 1:1 attention
- list of clients attending
- knowledge of clients' capabilities
- client training in use of steps and transferring
- proper attire for clients
- things clients need to bring
- medical approval (if needed) for client to attend

  IV. Pertinent Details
Vehicle Arrangements
- type and number of vehicles needed
- route information and directions
- number of drivers
- travel time

Dietary
- food needs
- dietary considerations
- cancel regular meal

Volunteers
- number of volunteers (ratio will vary depending on the type of outing)— never less than 1 volunteer for every 5 clients
- assign clients to volunteers for outings which require 1:1 attention

Accounting
- money from clients' accounts
- money from recreation budget

V.  Recreation
- write trip goals and objectives
- complete trip resource assessment
- complete arrangements concerning dates and times
- complete initial and final arrangements with the agency to be visited
- complete all arrangements within the facility
- compile final list of attendees
- publicize the event
- handle all situations away from the facility
- remember to take all of the little things such as sunscreen, towels, towelettes, hats, knife
- evaluate the event

## Health And Safety Factors

The clients' health and safety are the staff's number one priority.  No event which jeopardizes the health and safety of the client should be considered appropriate.  This is not to say activities should lack any element of risk and challenge.  Considering the lack of totally accessible sites, the client would never leave home if the staff did not take some risk.  The staff must weigh the level of accessibility and safety before scheduling an event.

*The accessibility check* will ascertain to a large degree the appropriateness of a site and what level of client may attend.  Good planning involves determining the safest way to make the experience fun for the client.  The following guidelines will help to make the experience safe as well as enjoyable.

Dress
- Are the clients dressed appropriately?  Will they be warm enough or too warm?
- Are they wearing pants which are short enough or tight enough around the waist to ensure they will not trip?
- Are they wearing appropriate shoes to avoid tripping or slipping?

Wheelchair
- Does the wheelchair have two foot rests?
- Are the footrests at the proper angle?
- Are the rubber strips around the wheelchair in good working order?
- Are there two hand grips?
- Are the brakes working properly?
- Is the wheelchair the appropriate size for the client?

First Aid
- Is the first aid kit on board?  Emergency procedures, and phone numbers?
- Are the emergency procedures in writing?  Have all of the volunteers and staff been trained in emergency procedures?
- Is a nursing staff member required to attend the outing?  (This is a good public relations too, for the recreation department.)

## Trip Essentials

The following checklist should be prepared and used on every trip away from the facility to assure the staff member in charge that they have the necessary items:

- directions
- emergency phone numbers
- sunscreen, hats
- towelettes, towels, paper towels
- diapers, lap robes
- sharp knife, scissors
- water—either cold or hot depending on weather conditions
- extra chairs or wheelchair

# SUMMARY

This work was divided into two sections. Chapters 1 through 8 explored the procedures for planning, scheduling, staffing, and evaluating a balanced therapeutic recreation program for older adults. Chapters 9 through 21 covered activities used by the authors or suggested by participants from the authors' many in-service programs to achieve the balanced program discussed in the earlier chapters.

Recreation activities must do more than fill idle hours. There is a growing need to provide quality programming based upon individualized client needs. These programs must be challenging and innovative to provide quality care that allows the client to express his/her individuality and maintain his/her dignity. Quality assurance involves analyzing the total recreation program to make sure all clients are involved in a well-balanced program of therapeutic recreation activities on a regular basis.

Client assessment is the first step in providing a quality program which is client-oriented. Assessment tools for achieving this end were discussed in Chapter 2. It is imperative that client participation and progress are evaluated and documented on a regular basis. Chapter 3 presented information to make writing goals and objectives more manageable, while Chapter 7 discussed evaluation procedures for staff and clients.

Many recreation program schedules appear adequate, but analysis often reveals that most of the programming involves relatively few clients. Chapter 4 explored the wide variety of factors that affect client participation. Suggestions for program formats, settings, and resources that go beyond scheduling only those activities that are "familiar and comfortable" were presented in Chapter 5. Chapter 6 explored the creative use of staff time and more effective use of volunteers that will result in an exciting program schedule with breadth and depth. Creative programming can be found with an on-site and community resources inventory in Chapter 8. Activities designed to promote participation were presented in Chapter 9. They take very little staff preparation time and although some of them are "one time" gimmicks, others may be useful on a regular basis to promote socialization.

Activity analysis usually reveals that sight and hearing are the two senses most often necessary for scheduled activities. Chapter 10 suggested activities which make use of the other senses also. Conversation and interaction activities were presented in Chapter 11. Many of the suggestions involve familiar activities from the past and simple skills which maximize social interaction among the participants. Chapter 12 addressed special techniques and problems involved in recreation programming for the confused client. Finding activities which are suitable and effective for these special people is a real staff challenge.

Many older adults avoid any activity which involves more than a minimum of movement. In order to encourage participation, the activity must be challenging, but not too strenuous. Chapters 13 through 15 explore how familiar activities may be adapted to provide enjoyment, and the challenge, as well as the benefits of exercise for the older person. Dramatics, story telling and music should be an integral part of a balanced recreation program. Chapter 16 explored some of the many possibilities for activities in these areas. Chapter 17 might have been called "Another Look at Crafts." Special attention was given to making things with a lasting value. Many of the projects prove useful in other programs or may be used as gifts to friends and families of clients. Before the advent of commercial toys and games, people enjoyed devising their own. Many of the projects in Chapter 18 are suitable games for 1:1's, small groups, or even a different type of carnival.

Most older people remember with great fondness their experiences with growing plants or gardening. However, many feel they can no longer participate because of the physical effort which would be necessary. Chapter 19 presented ideas which have been used successfully with older adults so they may continue to have the enjoyable experience of "growing things."

Special event ideas were presented in Chapter 20. Some special event problems were addressed and a number of innovative special event ideas were described. Trips and outings are a program area often overlooked, especially in residential settings. Suggestions for planning, scheduling, staffing and conducting this type of activity was presented in Chapter 21.

It is the hope of the authors that the reader will use the material presented to aid in the development of an innovative quality recreation program. This client-oriented approach utilized by a dedicated staff can do much to meet the ultimate goal of therapeutic recreation for the older adult–to keep the clients "alive" as long as they live!

## Additional Resources

Activity Director's Guide
Eymann Publications
1490 Huntington Circle
Box 3577
Reno, NV  89505

Bi-folkal Productions, Inc.
809 Williamson St.
Madison, WI  53703

Activities, Adaptions and Aging
Haworth Press, Inc.
10 Alice St.
Binghamton, NY  13904-1580

Hammatt Senior Products
P.O. Box 727
Mount Vernon, VA  98273

National Therapeutic Recreation Society
3101 Park Center Dr.
Alexandria, VA  22303-1593

Potential Developmential
775 Main St., Room 321
Buffalo, NY  14203

## BOOKS FROM VENTURE PUBLISHING

Acquiring Parks and Recreation Facilities through Mandatory Dedication: A Comprehensive Guide
by Ronald A. Kaiser and James D. Mertes

The Activity Gourmet
by Peggy Powers

Adventure Education
edited by John C. Miles and Simon Priest

Amenity Resource Valuation: Integrating Economics with Other Disciplines,
edited by George L. Peterson, B.L. Driver and Robin Gregory

Behavior Modification in Therapeutic Recreation: An Introductory Learning Manual
by John Dattilo and William D. Murphy

Benefits of Leisure
edited by B. L. Driver, Perry J. Brown and George L. Peterson

Beyond the Bake Sale—A Fund Raising Handbook for Public Agencies,
by Bill Moskin

The Community Tourism Industry Imperative—The Necessity, The Opportunities, Its Potential
by Uel Blank

Dimensions of Choice: A Qualitative Approach to Recreation, Parks, and Leisure Research
by Karla A. Henderson

Doing More With Less in the Delivery of Recreation and Park Services: A Book of Case Studies
by John Crompton

Evaluation of Therapeutic Recreation Through Quality Assurance,
edited by Bob Riley

The Evolution of Leisure: Historical and Philosophical Perspectives,
by Thomas Goodale and Geoffrey Godbey

The Future of Leisure Services: Thriving on Change,
by Geoffrey Godbey

Gifts to Share—A Gifts Catalogue How-To Manual for Public Agencies,
by Lori Harder and Bill Moskin

Great Special Events and Activities,
by Annie Morton, Angie Prosser and Sue Spangler

Leadership and Administration of Outdoor Pursuits
by Phyllis Ford and James Blanchard

The Leisure Diagnostic Battery: Users Manual and Sample Forms
by Peter A. Witt and Gary Ellis

Leisure Diagnostic Battery Computer Software
by Gary Ellis and Peter A. Witt

Leisure Education: A Manual of Activities and Resources
by Norma J. Stumbo and Steven R. Thompson

Leisure Education: Program Materials for Persons with Developmental Disabilities
by Kenneth F. Joswiak

Leisure Education Program Planning: A Systematic Approach
by John Dattilo and William D. Murphy

Leisure in Your Life: An Exploration, Third Edition
    by Geoffrey Godbey

A Leisure of One's Own: A Feminist Perspective on Women's Leisure
    by Karla Henderson, M. Deborah Bialeschki, Susan M. Shaw
    and Valeria J. Freysinger

Marketing for Parks, Recreation, and Leisure
    by Ellen L. O'Sullivan

Outdoor Recreation Management: Theory and Application
    Revised and Enlarged, by Alan Jubenville, Ben Twight
    and Robert H. Becker

Planning Parks for People, by John Hultsman
    Richard L. Cottrell and Wendy Zales Hultsman

Private and Commercial Recreation
    edited by Arlin Epperson

The Process of Recreation Programming Theory and Technique, Third Edition
    by Patricia Farrell and Herberta M. Lundegren

Quality Management Applications for Therapeutic Recreation
    edited by Bob Riley

Recreation and Leisure: An Introductory Handbook
    edited by Alan Graefe and Stan Parker

Recreation and Leisure: Issues in an Era of Change, Third Edition
    edited by Thomas Goodale and Peter A. Witt

Recreation Economic Decisions: Comparing Benefits and Costs
    by Richard G. Walsh

Risk Management in Therapeutic Recreation: A Component of Quality Assurance
    by Judith Voelkl

Schole VI: A Journal of Leisure Studies and Recreation Education

A Social History of Leisure Since 1600
    by Gary Cross

Sports and Recreation for the Disabled—A Resource Manual
    by Michael J. Paciorek and Jeffery A. Jones

A Study Guide for National Certification in Therapeutic Recreation
    by Gerald O'Morrow and Ron Reynolds

Therapeutic Recreation Protocol for Treatment of Substance Addictions
    by Rozanne W. Faulkner

Understanding Leisure and Recreation: Mapping the Past, Charting the Future,
    edited by Edgar L. Jackson and Thomas L. Burton

Wilderness in America: Personal Perspectives
    edited by Daniel L. Dustin

Venture Publishing, Inc
1999 Cato Avenue
State College, PA 16801
814-234-4561